Kid... ri... pass!
Solomon's ri... "men too...shall pass"
p.76-77

Bible
+ Abraham's store of healing
+ Miriam + leprosy
+ King Saul +
David's
music
(see p. 92?)

where is
hibodedus
in
Bible?
(private
tie?)

The Azamra Institute

The Azamra Institute is an independent, non-affiliated, non-profit organization devoted to communicating Jewish ideals in the languages and media of our times.

Azamra in Hebrew means "I will sing" (Psalms 146:2). This is the title of the basic teaching of the outstanding 18th century chassidic luminary, Rebbe Nachman of Breslov. "We must find the good in all people, especially ourselves. Each good point is a note in the song of life. This is the way to happiness."

- **Jewish Spirituality**
  Courses, seminars, study groups. Books. Tapes. Internet publishing. Jewish women's spirituality.

- **Health & Healing**
  Research and dissemination of authentic Jewish teachings on health and healing among healthcare professionals and the general public.

- **Haverim Outreach Network**
  Worldwide outreach to young people and the disadvantaged spreading knowledge and joy of the Jewish heritage.

Israel: P.O. Box 50037, Jerusalem
United States: 119 Rockland Center, Suite 148, Nanuet, NY 10954
Canada: Box 5696, Station A, 25 The Esplanade, Toronto, Ontario M5W 1N8
Britain: 102 Lyndhurst Court, London NW8 6EU

E-mail: info@azamra.org

Visit our website at: http://www.azamra.org

D1534669

A Call to Live

Jewish Guidance on Healing

For those facing illness and those who care for them,
and for people of all backgrounds and beliefs
who seek life, truth, peace, joy, health and healing

AZAMRA

About the ideas in this book

The Jewish tradition contains a wealth of guidance on all aspects of health and healing, physical, mental, spiritual, individual, societal and global. Teachings on these subjects are found in many places in the Bible, Talmud, Midrash, Halakhah, Kabbalah and Chassidut.

Outstanding among the many Torah sages who taught about healing are: the leading medieval codifier, philosopher and physician, Rabbi Moshe Ben Maimon, known as RaMBaM or Maimonides (1135-1204), and the towering mystic, sage, chassidic leader and story-teller, Rebbe Nachman of Breslov (1772-1810).

"A Call to Live" contains a variety of ideas and suggestions. All of them are based upon authentic teachings from within the Jewish healing tradition. "A Call to Live" seeks to explain some of the most important and relevant of these teachings in a simple, practical way in the language of today.

Those wishing to learn about the Jewish healing tradition in greater depth may consult "The Wings of the Sun: The Jewish Healing Tradition in Theory and Practice" by Avraham Greeenbaum, published by the Breslov Research Institute. This work provides full background information and sources for all the ideas and suggestions contained in "A Call to Live." For further details and information about how to order, see p. 119.

Contents

A Call to Live

1

A Call to Live

Many people never really appreciate what a blessing health is until illness or injury suddenly changes the course of their lives.

If you are ill, in pain, frustrated, anxious and despondent, you may feel that you have reached a very low point in your life. But it need not be so — if you are willing to hear the deeper message your illness or injury is sending you. It is a call to *live!* If your normal life has been disrupted, it is to teach you to be more fully aware of the preciousness of life, so that you will live your life with greater purpose each day and every moment up to the very last.

By heeding this call, you can transform what you are going through now into a profound learning experience that will open up new dimensions in your life and bring you to deeper fulfilment and happiness.

You surely want to heal in order to be able to achieve all your goals in life. Then don't wait until you are feeling better before you start living. There is no more effective way to encourage the healing process than by living your life to the full extent that you can *now*.

To be healed is to be able to live life to the full. Living well is a skill, which, like any other, can only be developed through practice. Practice *now!* Decide that you are going to live *now!* Making this decision is one of the most important steps you will take to recovery.

Living on a higher level

Physical and other limitations may make it difficult for you to continue with many of your usual activities at present. But don't grieve over what you can't do. Instead, think about all the things you *can* do to give meaning to your life at this time. Your physical limitations need not prevent you from living an active, fulfilling life on the mental and spiritual planes. These are precisely the levels within yourself that you should now seek to cultivate in order to be truly healed.

Be ready to explore new pathways of mind and soul. Learn how to relax and to meditate. Ponder the meaning of life in this universe. Reflect on your own destiny and purpose. Discover who you really are. Even if you are under stress owing to your physical condition, your medical treatment, emotional, financial or other pressures, be sure to avoid sinking into morbid anxiety and depression. Turn your pain and frustration into prayers. Try to see the positive side of what you are going through.

As you work on yourself, work also to enhance your relationships with others — your dear ones, friends, and all the other people with whom you have contact. If you are experiencing pain and hardship, learn from them to empathize with other people who may also be suffering. Even as you seek to fulfil your personal needs and pursue your purpose in life, take account of the needs and sensitivities of others. Develop your ability to communicate and live cooperatively with those around you. Be willing to learn from everyone.

Healing the Inner You

Many people think of healing as having to do mainly with the restoration of normal bodily functioning. It is certainly proper to do everything necessary on the physical level in order to bring about recovery. But medicine alone is not enough. That is because your body, crucial as it is to your existence in this world, is nevertheless only one part of an even greater whole: YOU.

You are a whole person with your own unique identity, your thoughts, feelings, emotions, needs, desires, memory, reason, imagination, goals, ideals, aspirations... as well as amazing untapped potential. The essential You, the living, thinking, feeling, creative "I" at the center, is what philosophers and psychologists call the "mind" or "psyche," while religious and mystical traditions call it the "soul" or "spirit."

A physical illness or injury obviously has far reaching effects on the mind and soul as well as on the body. Your bodily condition directly affects your mental states, your thoughts and feelings. However, the relationship is more than just one-way. Your mental and emotional states, your attitudes, your feelings about yourself and the way you run your life have a decisive influence on your level of physical health, your immunity to illness and injury, the extent to which your body is able to heal, and at what rate.

More than this, your mental, emotional and spiritual wellbeing are really the key to your overall happiness in life since your inner life is the very essence of your life. The health of your inner self — your mind and soul — is what makes the difference between a fulfilling, satisfying life and one that is not. There are people who may be technically fit and healthy physically, but they really have no life at all because their lives are wasted by emptiness and depression.

Your doctors may be treating you medically to try to cure your body. But as you wait and hope for your body to mend and heal, know that your inner personal healing — healing the bruises of your self and soul — is primarily in *your* hands. Since the mind and soul influence the body, the more you succeed in healing and cultivating your inner self, the greater your body's ability to heal. Therefore the most important contribution you can make to improving your physical condition is by working to heal and develop your inner self.

Life after life

There are times when the body cannot heal. Some conditions are chronic, others terminal. Everyone eventually ages and deteriorates physically, because in the end our bodies have to die. The body is a finite, material structure of limited duration: in due course it must disintegrate.

The body dies, yes, but the inner you never dies! The essential self and soul is non-finite spirit, and the spirit is everlasting. For the soul, death is not the end but a new beginning. Death is the gateway to a higher stage of life, a new state of being on a plane that we cannot even imagine as long as we are still in our bodies.

Death is death only in relation to the material world. But for the essential *you* — your soul — death is the stepping stone to a more exalted, more intense and vastly more joyous level of life on the spiritual plane. This is because of the greater ability of the soul to expand in the spiritual dimension when liberated from the physical body. If the prospect of death is awesome, this is because the soul then draws closer to the Source of all things — God — and God is awesome.

Illness may make us deeply aware of the great step that lies ahead of us. Sooner or later everyone must face this. A dangerous, life-threatening condition is a call to make your peace and come to terms with the prospect of death in order to use the time you have left in this world in the best possible way. Your body may be weak and in pain, but this need not crush your spirit. For the spirit is invincible.

Being willing to accept the prospect of death does not mean necessarily that you are going to die soon. Life and death are in the hands of God alone. No-one dies a moment before or after their appointed time.

You cannot control death, but that does not mean that you cannot choose how to live in the face of it. The idea is not to spend all your time morbidly preparing for death. On the contrary, you should shift from being a passive victim of fear and anxiety to actively taking charge of your life. Take stock of yourself. Work out your priorities. Drop whatever is meaningless and wasteful. Say what you want to say to your dear ones and friends. Fix what is in your power to fix in this world — and *live*.

Know that death leads to new life, and therefore you will never really die but only live. Now you are alive "here" in this world; afterwards you will be alive "there," on a higher plane. Whether you are "here" or "there," the main thing is to be alive! By deciding to live *now*, even within the limitations of illness or injury, you are making the most of your time "here" while at the same time preparing yourself in the best possible way for your life after life "there" later on.

Now!!!

Seriously ill or not, the fact is that in this world we are *all* condemned to death! None of us knows when his or her time will come. Sick or healthy, everyone can only benefit from accepting the fact of their own mortality. When we know that our time here is limited, we value it more and take full advantage of it.

Every single moment is precious. That is why you must live *now*. Don't put off living until tomorrow, saying "I can't live the way I want to right now because I'm not well: I'll wait till I'm better and *then* I'll start living." The day you are hoping for may never come, and even if it does, you do not really know what it may bring. In this world it is not possible for everything to be perfect. You have to carry on living even when things are not as you might want them to be.

You only have today! Discover how rich life can be right now, even amidst all your problems and difficulties. Find joy in whatever comes to hand. Prize each new insight you gain about life, especially those won through pain and suffering. Treasure times with dear ones and friends. Enjoy each act of kindness and love that you or others perform. Cherish each smile, each kind word, each good thought, each word of prayer and outreach to God. It is by living life *now* that you will heal, because this is precisely what healing is all about: living *now!*

> "Think only about today. When a person wants to live a spiritual life, it may seem like too much of a burden. But if you remember that you have only today, it won't be such a burden. Don't push off your spiritual life from one day to the next. For all a person has is the present day and the present moment."
>
> Rebbe Nachman of Breslov

2
The Secret of Health and Healing

The key to health and healing is ultimately simple: keep happy! *Simchah* — happiness and joy — is the elixir of the soul. And the health of the soul is the key to the health of the body.

It can take time and effort to attain true joy and self-fulfilment. The way to start is by making yourself happy with little things. Pamper yourself with small pleasures and comforts, good food and the like. Spend time with people who make you feel good. Lift your spirits with stimulating conversation and interesting reading. Listen to your favorite music. Joke. Laugh. Enjoy yourself!

This may work for a while, but you probably wonder how you can possibly be really happy when you are ill, in pain, confined to surroundings not of your choosing and troubled by many other problems. Even so, you must make every effort to find ways to be happy, even in face of all this adversity. Do everything possible to lift your moods.

For when you are happy, your mind becomes settled. You can then see things more clearly, and you will begin to understand the positive aspects of your present situation and your life in general, and uncover the good that exists even in adversity. This is the way to genuine happiness and fulfilment, which are the key to health and healing.

Why happiness promotes health and healing

Contemporary medicine is rediscovering the ancient truth that our mental and emotional states affect our bodies just us much as our bodily states affect our minds and feelings. The destructive effects on the body of excess tension, anxiety, negativity, frustration and depression are seen daily in heart, cancer and other clinics. Conversely, it is now well established that positive attitudes play a vital role in recovery, rehabilitation and long-term health.

To understand the reason for this, you must understand what keeps your body alive and functioning. The

> "The doctor should make every effort to see that everyone, sick and healthy alike, should always be cheerful and free of anxiety. This is the first priority in trying to heal anyone. The doctor should not imagine that he can improve people's mental states through his medical knowledge. The only way to achieve this is through spiritual guidance and teachings."
>
> Rambam

cells of the body grow, develop, reproduce, regenerate and maintain themselves to form organs and body systems of astonishing complexity and subtlety. Each individual cell and organ of the body goes through its own highly specialized sequences of biochemical reactions at its own unique pace.

The miracle is that all the individual rhythms of the different body cells, organs and systems are perfectly orchestrated. They work together to maintain overall stability and health in spite of constant fluctuations within the body and in the external environment. This balance is vital for the continuation of life.

What is it that makes unity out of the diversity of all the different bodily rhythms and functions? How are they all orchestrated? How is everything controlled? Physiology explains that our heart rate, breathing, digestion, excretory and other functions are regulated by the brain and nervous system. But if the body is under the control of the brain and the nerves, how are *they* controlled?

The brain and nervous system, and indeed the entire body, are subordinate parts of a greater system: the whole person. As soon as we consider bodily functioning in the broader context of the person as a whole, it becomes clear that, if we are to discover the master control system that ultimately sustains and governs our physical and mental functioning, we must search *beyond* the body and beyond the conscious mind.

The Soul

Religion and mysticism teach that the master control system is the soul. It is the presence of the soul that makes the difference between a living person and a dead body. People find it hard to form a clear conception of the soul. This is not surprising, since the soul is not something tangible like the hand, the heart or the brain. But although we cannot see or physically feel the soul, we do experience it directly on the level of our conscious awareness. The soul is "I," the sentient, feeling, thinking, purposeful ego sitting in the driver's seat of the body.

The soul is a complex system comprising a variety of subsystems. Some of them are accessible to our conscious minds, others are not. Thus the soul controls our bodily processes via the autonomic nervous system without our even being aware of it.

Even in the realm of our conscious behavior, we often do not know why we act the way we do. Our stream of everyday consciousness involves complex structures of highly subtle logical and non-logical thoughts, fantasies, intuitions, feelings and emotions that have roots stretching deep into our unconscious minds. In addition, we are usually quite unaware of the way in which higher, spiritual parts of our souls are quietly guiding our lives and destiny in this world.

For although the soul is "in" the body and therefore "in" the physical world, it is really rooted in a qualitatively different dimension of existence. The spiritual dimension interacts with the physical dimension yet it reaches way beyond it. You may have vague contact with these exalted spiritual levels at certain highly significant moments in life, as when you become subliminally aware that you are somehow being guided by a superior force. Such awareness sometimes comes in dreams, only to be lost on waking up.

The higher soul in each person is itself part of a far greater system that has its own master control. The ultimate master control over the entire creation is the mystery we call God.

Bodily rhythms and the music of the soul

How do the mind and soul actually control and influence the body? As we have seen, bodily functioning is a matter of rhythms. The rhythms of the various cells, organs and body systems are regulated and coordinated by other, higher order rhythms. These are the patterns of neural impulses relayed from one part of the nervous system to another. But how are these master rhythms controlled?

This can be understood by considering music. A piece of music is made up of a melody line with a rhythm. Usually the rhythm is the most infectious aspect of the music. Listen to a lively piece of music and see what happens. The rhythms created by the players travel in the form of the pulsating sound waves that cause your ear-drums to vibrate, thus penetrating your conscious and unconscious mind.

Before you know it, your hands and feet are tapping, your head is nodding to and fro, and your whole body is moving in unison under the sway of the rhythm. For the moment, the rhythm is "controlling" you and all your body movements.

Yet the rhythm of the music is itself subordinate to the melody line. Each melody has an inner quality that calls to be expressed appropriately through a suitable rhythm. So the rhythm is governed by the melody, which in turn is created by the mind of the master musician or composer. Through the melody and rhythm of the music, the composer "controls" the movements of all the musicians playing the music, the rhythmic tapping and swaying of the audience, and all the thoughts and feelings inspired in them by the music.

With the help of this analogy we may begin to grasp how the intangible, spiritual soul controls the tangible, physical body. Just as the body movements of the listener are influenced by the rhythms of a piece of music, so the functioning of individual body cells and organs is governed by the rhythms and patterns of the brain and neural impulses. These in turn are governed by a higher order control system: the melody sung by the soul.

The soul is the creator, conductor, player and singer of amazing "music." You may not always hear it, but it is this music that controls the rhythms of your brain and nervous system, sending you your thoughts, your feelings and your very life. In short, it's the music of your soul that makes you and your body tick.

What song are you singing?

What kind of song are you singing? Is it a happy song that is sending energy and vitality into every fiber of your being? Or has your inner music become hushed, muffled, sad and plaintive? Or is it tense, angry, aggressive and destructive?

Your mental states, your attitudes and general outlook have a direct effect on your body. Excess tension, anxiety, insecurity, anger, frustration, depression and other forms of negativity can cause distortions in your physical posture; they may restrict your breathing; they may drive you into poor dietary patterns, substance abuse and other destructive habits. Over time these may take a heavy toll on your joints and muscles, your arteries, heart, lungs and other vital organs, your digestion, nerves, immune system, general metabolism, resilience and vitality.

The weaker and more depressed the music of the soul, the more sluggish the metabolism becomes. This leaves the body less and less able to withstand regular wear and tear, let alone the ravages of illness or injury. But with happy music — positive attitudes, cheerfulness and joy — the entire system becomes invigorated and the functioning of all the cells and organs of the body is enhanced, bringing heightened physical immunity, increased stamina and greater wellbeing on every level.

> "When King Saul became afflicted with a depressed spirit, his attendants brought the young David to play to him. As David ran his hand over the strings of the harp and played, Saul found relief and felt good, and the evil spirit departed."
>
> I Samuel, 16:14ff

You must feed and nourish the cells of your body with the right songs: the happy, healing songs! The songs of life! This applies quite literally. Get into the habit of singing a happy tune. Hum inspiring melodies. Try! Experiment! Choose a favorite tune and work with it for five minutes. See what happens. At first your singing may feel a little uninspired, but if it's a good melody and you are prepared to "get into it," you'll soon see how the melody will start to lift you up, bringing you new vitality, greater optimism and more positive thoughts and feelings. Do this regularly! When you don't feel like singing yourself, have others sing or play to you, or listen to recordings of your favorite music.

The melody of life

It's not only tunes and songs in the literal sense that bring health and healing. You must turn your very life into a melody.

What is music? Music is made up of sequences of notes. To play music, you have to hit the right notes in the right order, one after the other. Each note is produced by air vibrations. If you don't know how to play, you may produce little more than a succession of strident noises. But a skilled musician can create profoundly stirring and inspiring music simply by moving artfully up and down the scale.

So too in all of life, every one of our thoughts, words or actions also produces "vibrations." Each one is a "note" in the total symphony of life and creation. How much "bad air" can be produced by one careless, cruel or selfish act, a single cutting remark or even an evil thought! Our syndromes of worry, fear, anger, frustration, depression and gloom create soul-grinding rhythms and melodies that destroy our bodies and our lives and those of the people around us.

But all this "bad air" can be dissipated, purified and sweetened by thinking good, positive, generous thoughts, by smiling, sharing a kind word, offering a helping hand.... There's always something good you can think, say or do.

The art of happiness is always to go for the good: to see the good points and pick out the good notes rather than harping on the bad. This applies to how you view the various situations you face in life and to the way you play out your roles in them. It applies to the way you look at and deal with the people around you. And it applies to the way you look at and deal with yourself. Each good point you find is a note in the melody of life.

Rejoicing in the good

It is natural to be happy in good times, when things are good and when you're feeling good. And if things are bad? In bad times, you have to *search* for the good. Have faith that good exists even in the worst adversity. Know that there is a way in which everything can be turned around for good. As King Solomon said, "On a good day, enjoy! And on a bad day, you must *look*"

(Ecclesiastes 7:14). In other words, when things are bad, you must look around and *search* until you discover the positive side.

Being positive does not mean you have to deny the truth. If you are in pain and discomfort, your suffering is very real. You don't have to pretend you're fine if you are far from it. Being positive means keeping yourself from sinking into a quagmire of morbid negativity by having faith in God's goodness even at the hardest moments.

You may face seemingly intractable situations in your life. You may feel locked in deep problems within yourself. But in many cases one of the best ways to improve a situation is by learning to look at it differently. The way you view things plays a major part in whether you experience them as good or bad.

> "Try hard to turn your very gloom and worry into joy. If you really set your mind to it, you'll soon find that even amidst the worst troubles and suffering there's an opening you can use to convert all the depression into joy. True joy is when you drag your darkness and depression even against their will and force them to turn into happiness."
>
> Rebbe Nachman

Use your mind and all the inner resources you possess to break out of negativity and depression and to be positive. You have the power to control and direct your thoughts. Don't allow yourself to be drawn into syndromes of negative thoughts and feelings. Find new, more positive ways of looking at yourself, other people and the various problems and difficulties you face. When bad thoughts come into your mind, make every effort to direct your thoughts elsewhere. Often the best way to put yourself in a better frame of mind is through humor and joking or acting a little silly.

Your laughter is the best medicine of all. Your happiness is vital. The life of your body and soul depend on it. For keeping happy is the key to good health, as it is to healing.

Having become sick, you must now make a special effort to pick yourself up and make yourself happy again. Turn the search for good into a way of life, because this is the key to happiness and fulfilment. Joy will enable you to focus on your true mission in this life and accomplish all that you must.

3
Where in the world am I?

When you wake up from your sleep only to feel pain all over your body... when you look around you, and even familiar surroundings seem strange and alien... and you rub your eyes and you ask yourself, "Where in the world am I?" this may seem like a question born of confusion and chaos. But in truth, asking this and other searching questions about the new reality you face in your life is a sign of an awakening mind and spirit.

Serious illness or injury may bring a welter of different thoughts and feelings, some so private that we cannot begin to share them with the healthy, chirpy people around us going about their business in such blissful ignorance of our own pain, shock, grief and anxiety. We may be bitter and angry: "Why *me*?" Perhaps we feel betrayed by our bodies. We worry about the future: "Will I suffer pain? Will I be permanently disabled or disfigured? Am I going to die? What's it like in the grave?"

It is right and natural to be seriously concerned about what is happening to you. But don't let anxiety push you into despair. Admitting physical vulnerability does not mean you will necessarily remain permanently weak from now on. Confronting the fact of your mortality does not mean you are going to die soon.

Your worries and concerns are in fact a signal to you to embark on an extensive examination of yourself and your life. You must now act as doctor to your own inner self. Just as a medical doctor first carries out a thorough examination and then prescribes treatment, so you should now take an honest inventory of yourself and your life. Then you must start developing your own self-healing strategy. This is your part in the healing process.

Don't think only about your physical condition and how you are going to get well. Consider also all the other issues in your life, including any problems within yourself, in your work, your relationships or other areas. Be ready to face things you might normally prefer not to think about. Be willing to ask the deepest questions — about your body and your soul, what this life is about, how you've been using your time, and how you'd *like* to use it in future. Where do you want to go? How are you going to get there?

Starting to work on yourself in this way is a major step forward on your self-healing journey. You'll come away with a new inner confidence founded upon greater wisdom and understanding. You'll be able to live your life more freely and joyously. And living is what healing is all about.

Who is in control?

For many people, the most frightening aspect of illness and death is the loss of control. After having been born helpless babies totally dependent on others, we gradually gained control of our hands and legs and our various faculties. We grew from childhood to adolescence and onwards, taking ever more control of our lives.

And then came the illness or injury... and suddenly we find ourselves helpless again, maybe to the point that we cannot even move. We hope that the doctors have things under control. But at times it seems as if everything is haywire — as if some wild force has taken charge and is beating us down time after time.

One of the things we have to learn to accept in this life is that sooner or later we are going to have to give up our control com-pletely. We all have to die, and death is the ultimate loss of control.

> "Why should you be afraid of dying? The world there is far more beautiful than here."
>
> Rebbe Nachman

For much of our lifetimes we are given a certain ability to direct and control things. Not that we can control everything. We can't fly. We don't choose our parents, our bodies, our minds and many other things. Yet there are major areas in which we do have a degree of control, if we choose to exercise it. In fact some of us put enormous energy into trying to manipulate other people and things in the hope of being able to keep various aspects of our lives under control.

But in the end we have no control. We may try to hold on for as long as we can. Sometimes death seems to stare us in the face, and we beg: "Not yet! Please! Let me get through just this one time!" But in the end there is no escape. Death is the ultimate loss of control. A dead body can do absolutely nothing for itself.

One of the greatest mysteries of this universe is how man enjoys his allotted time of glorious freedom — he flexes his muscles, runs out into the world and does what he wants... but at last his strength is exhausted, he shrinks back into second babyhood... and finally surrenders. His body becomes a useless clod that rots and turns to dust. All the pride and splendor are forgotten.... And then God is in control.

The Source

"God" is the English name for the ultimate Power that sustains and controls the entire cosmos and everything in it — from the furthest reaches, way way beyond the most distant of galaxies, right down to the smallest, finest details of creation, such as the eccentric, sauntering path of a single leaf that's fallen from the tree and is gently tossed and patted by a breeze until it comes to rest at its appointed place on earth, there to decay and merge back into the ecological cycle.

Take a few moments to think about the wonder of this universe. Think about the diversity and complexity of the natural world of plants, trees, insects, birds, animals, microorganisms, molecules, atoms, particles, waves, energies.... Consider the diversity of teeming humanity — all the different faces, types, ages, stages, activities, thoughts, feelings and secret inner worlds.... Think about this planet: the cities, plains, hills, mountains, forests, deserts, rivers, seas and oceans. Think of the moon, the sun, the stars... galaxies upon galaxies stretching out for endless millions of light-years, further and further away... until the human mind is totally overwhelmed and you have to turn your thoughts to something more immediate and graspable.

The divine Being that sustains this unimaginable richness and diversity is utterly beyond the power of the human mind to envisage or understand. Jewish tradition refers to the ultimate Power that is the source and cause of all existence as *Eyn Sof*. The Hebrew means "No End!" The human mind is only able to grasp things that are finite, i.e. things that have limits and boundaries. But *Eyn Sof* is literally *without end* — beyond all limits — and therefore cannot be conceived in any way.

This amazing universe is not an accident. It is a system, albeit one so vast that our minds could never grasp it, though at times, when we experience certain quirks of fate, strange coincidences, mysterious happenings, beautiful serendipity and the like, we may be granted a faint glimpse of how everything ultimately fits together.

The unity that underlies the entire universe is expressed in the main name of God in the Bible: *YHVH* (traditionally pronounced as *Adonai* when praying, or as *Yud Keh Vav Keh* when referring to the name at other times). The Hebrew root of this name is *HaVaH*, which means "is" or "exists." The name *YHVH* signifies "the

One that *causes* existence or being," i.e. the *Source* of all phenomena on every level, a Power beyond space and time, One that *has been* always, *is* now in the present, and *will be* for ever and ever.

Another biblical name of God is *Elohim* (pronounced as spelled when praying, but referred to at other times as *Elokim*). This name signifies that the One God is the supreme power underlying and controlling all the multiplicity of different powers manifested in the universe.

Refining your understanding of God

In childhood many people develop their own images of God, only to reject them as they grow older and find them inconsistent with what they have learned about the way in which the world seems to work. Modern science has made some traditional conceptions of God appear primitive. Many find it

"People have many difficulties with the idea of God, such as 'How could a loving God create suffering and evil?' or 'How can we be free when God knows what we will do?' Yet it is only fitting that God should be surrounded by mystery. God is so exalted that it is totally beyond our ability to grasp the hows and whys of providence. If God's ways were in accordance with the demands of our meager understanding, that would mean there would be no difference between God's mind and ours."

Rebbe Nachman

hard to relate to conceptions of God as a kind of super-person who "speaks," "creates," "works miracles" in nature, in history, and the like.

Religious traditions frequently refer to God as "Father." This may be problematic for those who have experienced difficulties in their relationships with parents. Some resent the idea of God as a ruler with a set of laws telling people how to behave. The image of a strict, reproving, chastizing God may be perceived as a repressive threat to one's freedom to make one's own choices in life. Some reject the authority of religion because in their experience it has been falsely invoked by human beings to serve their own mundane interests.

The rejection of false and outworn images of God is indeed necessary in order to develop a more mature conception that will aid rather than inhibit us in our personal growth and development. Sometimes childhood ideas about God remain embedded deep within us. It may take a conscious effort to exorcise them in order to reach a higher understanding. Thus the young Abraham, founding father of Judaism, smashed the idols in his father's house before setting off alone on his journey to the Land of Israel — a journey that was really into his own self and soul.

Ultimately each person must find his or her own way to conceive of and relate to the supreme Source of this universe and of our very lives. Re-examining our ideas about God in the light of authentic Jewish teachings on the subject can help us clarify and deepen our understanding.

Choices and consequences

Whether we like it or not, ultimately God (however we understand God) *is* in control. We cannot control death, and there are many other circumstances in our lives that are chosen for us, such as the family and socio-economic group we are born into, our bodies, minds and other endowments, and the many other external and internal factors that leave their imprint on us down to our very core.

Yet amazingly, within these parameters we are free. Far from being a repressive tyrant, God gives us complete control over vital aspects of our lives and destinies. It is up to you whether you put your time, energy, money and other resources into food, drink, sex, work, play, household, family and other relationships, hobbies, sports, entertainment, art, intellectual development, spiritual growth, service of others or anything else. It is up to you whether to strive to make the best of the advantages and disadvantages you've been given, or to rail against fate and say "to hell with trying."

You are free to choose. And then you must live with the consequences of your choices. No matter what you do or don't do in life, there are always consequences of one kind or another. Every one of your choices leaves its mark on your body, your soul, the quality of your life and the lives of those around you.

Our predicament as human beings is that while we have no option but to make choices, the long-term effects of our decisions are usually unknown at the moment we actually make them. Science may provide information about the probable effects of certain courses of action. But science can tell us nothing about whether they will bring happiness and fulfilment.

It is our very inability to know in advance the long-term consequences of our choices that gives the real edge to our freedom. If at the very outset we already knew the evil consequences of wrong choices, we would never make them.

Taking responsibility

As you take stock of yourself and survey your life, you must take responsibility for any poor choices you may have made. Consider carefully whether your own behavior may have been a factor leading to your present illness or other undesirable aspects of your life. This does *not* necessarily mean that you bear responsibility for causing these problems. Many of the things that happen to us are sent by God for reasons that cannot be understood in worldly terms.

Yet there are also many cases where people's lifestyle, attitudes and behavior *do* cause or contribute to their problems, including actual physical illnesses. The point is not to grieve over your past mistakes, but rather to admit them honestly in order to take responsibility for your life and make wiser choices from now on.

But how can you make wise choices when you don't always know what the consequences of your choices are going to be? The Torah — God's teaching to mankind — gives us guidance about good choices to make at each of the different junctures in our lives in this world, from birth to death.

The Torah views human life from the perspective of eternity. We are more than merely people living here and now in this world. Each one of us is a soul with roots and branches stretching out into the entire cosmos, a soul that has existed for much longer than we can remember, a soul that will be alive and aware long after our bodies are dust.

God is good. Good is by nature expansive: good seeks to spread itself. Thus God desires to bestow good on all creation. God wants every single soul to have the very best — eternal good. And God wants it to be our very own. Thus God placed us here in a world where we have to *earn* the good for our souls through our own efforts.

In a world filled with falsehood and confusion, our mission is to strive to do good and be good, and thereby know God, who is all good. Our actions in this world affect not only our lives here but also the destiny of our souls in higher realms after death. The soul enjoys the good earned in this world for ever.

The Torah gives guidance as to how to earn this eternal good by following simple pathways of conduct in practical, everyday life. We should eat and satisfy our other needs in moderation, with gratitude on our lips. We should show kindness and compassion to others. We should conduct our business affairs with honesty and integrity. We should strike a balance between work and recreation, celebrating Shabbat and festivals... And so on.

The Torah prescribes and suggests, but the actual choice remains ours. We see no police going around compelling people to be kind, give charity, pray, observe Shabbat, follow the dietary rules, etc. The Torah code is "advice" which everyone is totally free to take or ignore as they choose — and live with the consequences of their decisions.

Faith

Do you believe in the medical treatment you are receiving? If you do, is it because you yourself are a medical expert and you *know* that the treatment is bound to work? Or do you have *faith* (or hope) that the doctors know what they are doing?

In critical areas of our lives there are many things we have to take on trust. This certainly applies in healing the inner self. It takes a leap of faith to believe that Torah pathways of kindness, charity, prayer, meditation, Shabbat and so on can bring inner healing and fulfilment.

No scientist can measure the greater sense of meaning and happiness to which these pathways lead. Fulfilment in life and connection with the divine are levels of experience barely discussed by science. But that doesn't make them any less real and important to you.

God is on a plane that science cannot reach because science deals only with phenomena that can be experienced with our physical senses. God, as the ultimate cause and source of these phenomena, cannot be experienced directly.

Knowledge of God comes not from scientific enquiry but through the stance or mental attitude we call faith. People often find their faith to be confirmed by what they see around them. But you don't get faith because you've seen proof. First you have to decide to have faith; understanding comes later.

To have faith is to have the humility to admit that there are mysteries about our existence in this world that our minds cannot understand. The essence of faith is to believe that everything we see around us is part of one vast, single, unified system that encompasses many other planes of existence besides the material world with which we tend to be so preoccupied.

Interpenetrating this material world of space and time are emotional, intellectual and spiritual realms that are also called "worlds." Life in this world is one leg of a journey that leads to a higher plane of existence in the "next world." Belief in the afterlife is one of the fundamentals of Judaism.

It is this faith that gives meaning to many aspects of life here in this world that would otherwise be incomprehensible. In terms of this world, injury, illness and death are the antithesis of life. They signify destruction and the negation of life as we know it. Why should people have to work and struggle so hard and endure so much in their lives, only to end up helplessly ravaged by pain, suffering and physical destruction before finally dying? Often the end of life is like a shipwreck that makes everything seem so futile.

But what to our eyes seems like meaningless suffering is a cleansing of the soul in preparation for its eternal journey. What we see as death is in fact a transition to a new state of being. When the time comes for the inner self and soul to move forward, the worn body, having served its purpose, is discarded like the skin of a caterpillar, while the soul takes wing and flies to new horizons.

From our perspective in the material world it is impossible to imagine what this new, higher life might be like. But deep inside, the soul knows its destiny. This is why it happens that at critical moments in our lives we naturally begin to wake up and ask, "Who am I? Where did I come from? Where am I going?"

The destruction wrought by injury, illness and death is not purposeless. It is to enable the soul to build anew on a higher level. Having this faith will enable you to live more happily in *this* world, because you will know in your heart of hearts that all your struggles, efforts, pain and suffering have meaning and purpose. If pain and illness are the antithesis of life in this world, they will lead to a higher level of synthesis and harmony in the world to come.

People ask: "Why did this illness or injury happen to *me*?" But what has happened is a fact you cannot change. What you *can* change is the way you live your life in the face of your problems and difficulties. And this way you can change the meaning they have in the wider canvas of your life as a whole.

As soon as you accept your present condition as a necessary stage in your spiritual journey, you can learn to *use* it for your long-term growth and development.

Be yourself

Faith means more than having faith in God "out there." You must have faith in the God who is with you here and now: the God within your heart and your innermost self. You must have faith in the divinity contained within your highest hopes and aspirations, in your finest traits and faculties, in your subtle thoughts and feelings.

You must have faith that you are important and what you do in this world matters. The goodness you bring into this world is very precious. Your struggle is important and worthwhile.

Have faith in the power and resourcefulness of your soul and its incredible capacity to heal. For the soul is invincible.

One of the most amazing features of the creation is that everything is unique, down to the smallest detail. God is a master artist who loves originality. Nothing displays the infinite power of divinity more spectacularly than the uniqueness of every blade of grass, and especially the uniqueness of every human being, each with his or her unique individuality.

Because you are unique, you have to find your own unique way of relating to God and developing the divine spark within yourself. You must develop your own understanding of how to apply traditional spiritual guidance in *your* life and circumstances. God dwells with each person in the very place and situation in which they find themselves. God "hears" them there, and subtly guides them in their chosen path in order to bring them to their ultimate goodness and fulfilment.

To be yourself, you must discover who you really are and clarify what you want in your life. Our upbringing and life experiences often leave us with a tough protective mask that we wear even to ourselves. It gives us a certain identity, outlook, opinions and attitudes. But deep inside us there is a sensitive, often wounded inner self that may have been repressed and stunted owing to background, upbringing and other factors. We have to tend and nurture that inner self. We must have the courage to be who we really are and *live*.

In the revelation at Mount Sinai, God introduces Himself as "*I am.*" "I am *YHVH* your God who brought you out of the land of Egypt..." (Exodus 20:2). It can be disconcerting to realize that God is a live "personality," as it were, with a "self," an "I," just like we have. Some people experience this as a threat to their own independence, which is why they prefer an impersonal God or none at all. But in the end we all have to acknowledge that God alone can say "I." "I kill and I make alive, I wound and I heal, and there is no-one that can deliver out of My hand" (Deuteronomy 32:39).

The inner reality of that divine "I" is totally beyond the grasp of the human mind. But even so, as long as we are alive, we *do* have some idea of what it is, because each one of us is also an "I." Within limits, we too are free to create and control. Only the all-powerful God could create an independent being — an "I" — that can also create and control. The inner "I" — the soul — is the most Godly part of us.

God's intention was not that this "I" of ours should be timid and repressed. We must be humble, yes. We have to know our limits. We have to know where our power comes from. But true humility is to rejoice and exult in the gift of power and creativity that God has given us. God wants us to *use* this power to create!

Whether you know it or not, control of your destiny is in your hands. Wake up to your freedom and grasp the reins of control. Take your life in your hands and direct yourself to where you want to go.

Set your goals and work towards them! It is the process of striving to attain your goals, with all the ups and downs this involves, that will bring you true happiness and satisfaction in life.

4

The Three Points of Empowerment

Medical treatment is the more passive part of the healing process. In many cases the patient is asked to do little more than submit to the treatment and wait for it to take effect. But the most important part of your *total healing* — healing and vitalizing the inner you — obviously cannot come about through remaining passive. *You* must take the initiative. *You* have to act.

There is widespread agreement today that changes in diet, lifestyle, attitudes and other areas may play a major role in recovery and long-term health. But many people find it hard to make even relatively small changes in their lives. One of the main reasons is often because inside they feel hurt, tired, cynical and despondent. Why make the effort to change if you don't believe it will make you genuinely happier?

Too often people just give up on themselves. They feel helplessly locked into negative attitudes and behavior patterns. Aren't we all too familiar with the repeated vicious cycles that consume our lives? We may not want to so much as glance at our inner mirror. It's easier to reach for that snack, open a magazine, pick up the phone, pour a drink, light a cigarette, throw ourselves into our work or other activities, or just go to sleep... anything rather than face the deeper issues in our lives.

But these unresolved issues and the accompanying inner pain can be major factors underlying poor health and illness. To allow yourself to remain locked in the same old patterns could be a recipe for disaster. If you want real recovery and a life worth living, you *must* find ways to make the necessary changes in your life and in your inner self.

There are three "power points" or sources from which you can draw the inner strength necessary for growth and change. These are three crucial points of interaction between yourself and sources of help and support. The first is the point of interaction between you and those you choose as your *guides* in life. The second is the point of interaction between you and the *friends* whose support you need. Third, and most important, is the point of interaction between you and your own *inner self*. These are the three points of empowerment.

> "You should talk over spiritual matters with your teacher in order to receive guidance and inspiration from the teacher's 'point.' You must also discuss these matters with a friend in order to receive from your friend's unique 'point.' Finally, you must draw power from your own inner 'point' through meditation and prayer."
>
> Rebbe Nachman

In each case the essential quality of the interaction involved is one of give-and-take. When you accept counsel and guidance from a teacher, it means giving something. You have to give yourself, in the sense of submitting to the advice and putting your energy into following it. Paradoxically, this giving on your part is actually receiving. What you get back is the new power you gain from your teacher's wisdom and insights and from correct practice of the skills and techniques he or she instills you. It's like when you exercise: the more effort you invest, the healthier and stronger you become.

Gaining friendship and support likewise depends on giving. The more support you give to others — through empathy, kindness, sharing and so on — the more support you will find you receive. By making some good friends and opening up to people who can help you in various ways in your chosen pathway, each one of your interactions with them becomes a "power point" from which you yourself can receive greater inner strength.

Giving is also necessary in order to draw greater power from your own higher self. Here, what you have to "give" is some of your *time.* You must make time for meditation and other practices that can increase your inner power. When working on yourself in these ways, you are at the "point" of encounter and give-and-take with your own higher self. As you learn to work on yourself in the right ways, you will receive rich dividends of inner power and joy in return for all your time and effort.

1. Guidance

The Rabbis said: "Get yourself a teacher and acquire a friend" (*Avot* 1:6). In advising us to find a teacher, they understood that human beings have a basic need for guidance in life.

Small children need a guiding hand to help them find their way safely around the physical and social environment. All of us — even adults — are little children in this amazing, divinely-created cosmos. We all have limited vision. We are all prone to make mistakes. Often we simply do not know what is best for us. Few people have the power to release themselves from their own inner weakness and constriction without some external source of true guidance and inspiration. Anyone who wants to make the most of their life needs someone of greater experience and wisdom to teach them.

You need someone who cares for your true good, understands what you really need, and knows how to give it to you. Such a person is not always easy to find. But even if you cannot find your own ideal guide in the flesh right now, you can always turn to the great classics of guidance and

> "What is the remedy for those who are sick in their souls? They must go to the wise. For the wise sages are the doctors of the soul, and they have the power to bring healing to the soul through teaching better attitudes and behavior."
>
> Rambam

inspiration, such as the Bible or the teachings of outstanding spiritual masters like Rebbe Nachman.

Empowerment from such teachings comes through reading and re-reading them, pondering their meaning, and thinking carefully about how they apply to *you*. As you review favorite teachings over and over again, key words and phrases will become imprinted within you, giving you greater strength to face up to the challenges in your life.

Opening up your heart

Even so, reading books is not enough. You also need someone real and alive to talk to about your goals and ambitions and about how you can overcome the obstacles that stand in your way. You need someone who can talk back to you and provide you with greater perspective and practical guidance.

People sometimes dream of having their own ideal mentor in life, but it may turn out that the people who become your actual guides will be different from what you imagine. If you put your mind to it, you could probably think of several people to whom you could turn for help and support. You may not always feel willing to follow all the advice you receive. But the very act of airing issues with another person can help you clarify what you do want to do.

Some people talk to their rabbis. For others it may be a therapist, a counsellor, a lawyer, an old aunt, or just someone who impresses you because of the way they live their life. All you have to do is ask the person you have in mind if they would give you some private time.

Make an effort to overcome any inhibitions you may have about opening up. Be willing to drop your masks and defenses. Admit your inner tenderness and sensitivity. Talk out your fears and worries, your hopes and desires. Tell your life story. Share your pain and grief, your tears, your laughter and fun times.

Talk about your mistakes. Admitting your mistakes and weaknesses to someone else can provide you with a more objective perspective on yourself, helping you to develop greater self-understanding and to make better choices in the future.

There are mistakes and there are also sins. Be willing to admit that some of the things you have done in your life may have been truly sinful — against family, friends and associates, against God, and against your very own self!

Whether you need to talk about sins, mistakes, personal hurt and pain, fears, worries, confusion, loneliness or any other private burden, you can only benefit from insight and guidance from the right person. Nothing is more therapeutic than to open yourself to someone with whom you feel secure, someone who listens with true empathy and really cares about what's best for you.

In order to heal your inner self, seek out a doctor for your soul. Some people can benefit from long-term counselling or therapy. For others, periodic discussions with a mentor combined with reading the right books may be sufficient. Overcome your pride and hesitations and go to a guide for help. By giving yourself, you will be receiving. For in return you will gain a world of inner power.

2. Support

In the same breath as the Rabbis said, "Get yourself a teacher," they also said, "Acquire a friend." The two ideas are closely bound together. A true teacher is your best friend, while a true friend can be your best teacher.

One of the main differences between a relationship with a spiritual guide and one with a friend is that the latter is more reciprocal. Sometimes you receive from your friend, sometimes your friend receives from you. Each of you has his or her unique inner "point" from which the other can receive.

The friend may be an old chum, your spouse, a brother or sister, or someone else you love dearly. It might be someone you've known for a long time. It could be somebody new. Illness or injury can often be the catalysts to help us make new friends or see fresh sides of old ones. People with specific problems can often find friendship through support groups for those with the same problem. Others may wish to build their own support circle.

Friendship plays a special role in healing (which is why the Jewish tradition places such emphasis on visiting the sick, *bikur cholim*). Social isolation is a major underlying factor in many illnesses. There is a human need to share thoughts and feelings, especially in relation to traumatic events. When this need is not met, feelings fester, putting chronic stress on the heart, the nerves, the immune and other systems. Friendship is one of the main keys to actual physical health as well as to emotional and spiritual balance.

A true friend is very precious. A friend is someone you can open up to freely without having to hide behind a mask. You know that your friend will accept who you are and what you are saying with love and respect. The ideal friend is one who wants your true good and will therefore not hold back from giving you honest feedback for fear of hurting your feelings.

Opening yourself up to such a person is empowering because it helps you to be yourself. Talking things out with your friend can give you a better understanding of what you really feel inside and what you really want. When you give expression to your highest aspirations and discuss the changes you want to make in your life, this can help you actually make them. Good friends can support and encourage each other to eat more healthily, persist with their fitness programs, practice meditation, deepen their faith and many other things.

How to "buy" friends

It's not the number of friends you have or how much time you spend with them that counts so much as the quality of your relationships. The kind of friend who is a real support is worth buying! That is why the Rabbis said, "*Acquire* a friend."

Paradoxically, many people who seem to be surrounded by friends are actually very lonely and feel they have no-one to whom they can really turn. Some do indeed try to "buy" friends — with gifts, flattery, or by trying to impress them. But these methods of seeking closeness may be self-defeating, merely setting you further apart from the very people whose friendship you seek.

When the Rabbis spoke about buying a friend, they were talking about payment of a different kind. The way to buy friends is through *giving* friendship. To get a good friend, *be* a good friend. Be to others the kind of friend you yourself would like to have.

When you look at other people, try to see the inner person behind the face. Many people desperately crave a little understanding, kindness and encouragement. Take an interest in who this person really is rather than only thinking about what you want from him or her. Project yourself into their situation. What do they need? What are they searching for? What could you give

> "With happiness you can give a person life. A person might be in terrible agony and not be able to express what is in his heart. There is no-one to whom he can unburden his heart, so he remains deeply pained and worried. If you come to such a person with a happy face, you can cheer him up and *literally give him life*. This is a great thing and by no means an empty gesture."
>
> Rebbe Nachman

them that will genuinely benefit them? The effort to understand and sympathize with others will also help you understand yourself better and be kinder to yourself.

A second kind of giving necessary in order to "buy" deeper friendship and intimacy with someone is giving *yourself*, in the sense of taking the risk of lowering your outer walls and letting your tenderer sides be seen. When you have the courage to lower your outer walls and disclose more of your real self, warts and all, your friends will feel safer about showing their real selves too.

If you are recovering from illness or injury, this is a good time to seek to heal relationships with your dear ones and other people you are close to. Healing your relationships is an important part of healing yourself.

The way to heal relationships is through seeking open and honest communication. Communication must be two-way. Get into the habit of expressing clearly what you think and feel so that the other person can understand you better. And you must also listen intently to what *they* are saying, avoiding the tendency to judge harshly or jump to hasty conclusions. Rather, you should seek to empathize. What are they *really* expressing? What inner feelings lie behind their words and gestures? When you show a willingness to understand others, it will make them more willing to understand you.

Learning to communicate better does not mean you have to be totally open and defenseless to all people at all times. Not everyone is mature enough to understand or accept your more vulnerable side. Not everyone is capable of giving you the friendship and support you need. Some people might knowingly or unknowingly hurt you or take unfair advantage of you. The friends you need are those who understand your needs and sympathize with the steps you want to take to make changes in your life. Choose your friends carefully.

When you find the right friends, talk together frankly and honestly about the things you each want in life. Share some of your more private thoughts and feelings. Speak about your hopes, your fears and concerns. Think together about how you might be able to alleviate some of your concerns. How can you be more positive and joyous even if things are very hard? Affirm your faith together. Encourage each other. Discuss practical steps you can each take to move closer to your respective goals.

It is this give-and-take between friends that empowers. With the support of others, you can accomplish things you would not ordinarily be able to do on your own. Friendship and support — whether from individuals or from a group — can give you a greater sense of meaning in your life and help you feel more connected with the world, with yourself and with God. This will make it easier for you to turn inwards in order to draw new power from your own inner point. This is the third point of empowerment.

3. Your own Inner Point

Your inner "point" is the creative source of all of your mental, emotional and spiritual life. It is what religion and mysticism call the soul: an invisible, ever-renewed wellspring of vitality and inspiration from which you can draw at all times and in all circumstances in order to grow, heal and lead a richer, more meaningful life.

Turning to your own inner point means getting in touch with yourself and learning to draw upon your inner resources in order to attain your most precious goals. You must take a calm look at yourself and your life. You must think seriously about who you really are and where you stand. What do you want to accomplish? How are you going to succeed?

Going to your inner point involves working on yourself in different ways in order to enhance your mental states, improve your outlook and cleanse yourself of negativity. You may have to go deep into the innermost recesses of your being. You must learn to make any necessary changes in your life and to direct yourself to what you want to achieve. In this way you become more proactive. You take greater control of your life instead of being swept along by surrounding currents.

Turning to your inner point also means looking far beyond yourself — reaching out to the Higher Power that is the source of the whole universe and of your very life. You make direct contact with the Divine — whether through inner quieting and "listening," or more actively, through prayer and other forms of self-expression. Illness or injury may confront you with some very serious issues. Turning to God will help you face everything, and you will grow and elevate yourself in the process.

Learning how to draw a steady flow of inner power from the "point" within your own self is a crucial part of self-healing. Otherwise, insights may come to you but you may do little with them. You may make decisions and resolutions but find it hard to follow them through.

To draw power from your inner "point," you must take *time*. If you want to keep your body fit and strong you have to make time for regular exercise. In the same way, to keep fit mentally and spiritually you need to set regular sessions in which to practice the techniques that lead to inner growth and spiritual connection.

In the Jewish tradition, the word for this private time is *hisbodedus*. So central is the place of hisbodedus in health and healing that it deserves a chapter to itself.

5

Hisbodedus: Time for Yourself

The literal meaning of the Hebrew word *hisbodedus* is "making oneself alone." The aim is not to become a hermit. In essence, hisbodedus is private time that you put aside for yourself on a regular basis. You detach yourself from your normal routine for a while in order to explore and develop yourself through meditation, introspection, self-expression, talking, praying, singing and any other method that helps *you*.

Hisbodedus is alluded to in various places in the Bible. In different forms it was taught by many Jewish spiritual teachers through the ages. It was given special emphasis by Rebbe Nachman of Breslov. Some of the main techniques that may be used in hisbodedus are discussed in more detail below.

The mark of a successful hisbodedus session is that you should feel *good* at the end of it. At the very least, you should feel better than before! Sometimes this is achieved through relaxation, breathing, settling the mind, etc. At other times more active methods may be employed, as described later.

The hisbodedus session itself may not necessarily be calm throughout. In one and the same session you may go through a whole gamut of different experiences, from heightened consciousness, insight, joy, gratitude, peace of mind and divine connection to frustration, inner pain, grief, tears and many more. Be willing to face negative aspects of yourself and your life honestly and with the confidence that God can help you discover the good concealed within negativity and darkness. Searching for this goodness will bring you to greater harmony and joy.

Aim to set aside time for yourself every day. This could be anywhere from about ten minutes to as much as an hour, according to your needs. Surely you deserve it!

When and where

Choose a time when you are not likely to be disturbed. Many people prefer to practice hisbodedus early in the morning before the pressures of the day build up. Some take a break for hisbodedus between

---

"Hisbodedus is the highest level of all. It is greater than everything else. Fix a time to go off by yourself to some room or meadow and express your thoughts and feelings to God in your own words. Pour out your whole heart to God, including your regrets and contrition about the past and your yearning to come closer in the future, each person according to his level. This is the best way of coming close to God because it includes everything else. No matter what is lacking in your spiritual life, even if you feel totally remote from God, talk it out and ask God to help you. Practice hisbodedus regularly every day. Then be happy for the rest of the day."

Rebbe Nachman

activities. Others practice hisbodedus at the end of the day, finding that it helps them unwind. For best results, choose a time when you have not just eaten a large meal as this may interfere with your mental clarity. If you are unable to sleep at night, you might try some hisbodedus then.

If possible, find a place where you can have some privacy. If you are confined to bed, you can practice hisbodedus right there. If you are up and about, choose a quiet corner whether at home or elsewhere. Natural surroundings can be especially conducive to calm and spirituality. If you have access to a suitable natural spot, or even your own back yard, take full advantage of it!

Before you begin a session of hisbodedus, it is a good idea to decide in advance how long you want the session to last, e.g. fifteen minutes, half an hour, etc. Have a clock or timer handy.

Make yourself as comfortable as possible. There is no required posture for hisbodedus. Choose a posture that you find conducive to relaxation and clarity. Many people find it best to practice hisbodedus sitting in a comfortable chair with the back well supported. If you wish, you may stand or walk about. Lying down is acceptable, especially if you are tired or not feeling well. However, at other times lying down is not recommended as it may make you drowsy.

Now you are ready to begin.

Settling the mind

Simply sitting quietly in a relaxed state can free your mind and help you get in touch with your thoughts, feelings and creative powers. One by one you let go of your tensions and they drop away, leaving you with a blessed feeling of profound calm, liberation, clarity, enhanced sensitivity and alertness. It becomes easier to think, understand, remember things and work out problems. New insights may result, together with a growing awareness of the spiritual dimension of life.

The benefits of deep relaxation are so great that it is well worth spending a little time learning the technique. Initially you may have to concentrate more on bodily relaxation. Once you have mastered this, you will be able to enter the relaxed state virtually at will and have full enjoyment of the mental, emotional and spiritual benefits it can bring.

If you wish, start with a few stretches. If you are confined to bed you can practice relaxation lying down. Otherwise, sit erect with your head comfortably balanced and your eyes closed. Focus your attention on the different parts of your body in order, one by one, from the feet upwards. Which muscles are tense? The key to relaxing is to understand that no effort is called for. Simply let go of tension. If you become restless, stretch and move around a bit, or take a few deep breaths, and then go back to quiet sitting.

To relax deeply, you must also let go of the inner fear, anxiety, anger, resentment and other factors that so often cause people to tense various parts of their bodies. The way to overcome fear is by having faith that everything in your life is in God's hands, and God is good and wants your good.

The active phase of hisbodedus

Some people hold that within each individual there are natural wellsprings of vitality and joy ready and waiting to flow forth, and if you can only relax and settle your mind sufficiently, the happiness will naturally bubble up within you.

However, this fails to take into account how hurt, wounded, thwarted and stunted many people are inside as a result of what they have been through in their lives. This is why some people find that when they start meditating, disturbing thoughts and feelings begin to surface, or they feel gray and cloudy and want to go to sleep.

In order to draw out, nurture and actualize the true power of your inner "point," it is not sufficient merely to relax and try to settle the mind. It is also necessary to work on yourself actively in order to overcome inner forces that may be inhibiting this latent power.

After an initial period of quiet sitting, a typical hisbodedus session turns into a workshop in which you contemplate what is happening in your mind, your heart and your life as a whole. Then you actively start working on yourself in order to change and grow.

The power of words

Your most powerful tool for change, growth and spiritual connection is right under your nose. It is your mouth. Just as you can influence others by the way you speak to them, so you can affect your own self. With the right words, songs, cries and other means of expression, you can influence your own states of mind and direct yourself to where you want to go.

Small children quite innocently express themselves out loud — to God, to themselves, to invented characters, or to no-one in particular. But as we grow older this easy self-expression tends to become muted, turning into the continual, and often negative, internal dialogs within our minds. Sometimes our innermost thoughts and feelings go underground and may be hidden from our very selves.

Talking to yourself is popularly considered a sign of madness. Perhaps it is when the person is not in control of it. But one of the sanest things you can do to enhance your life is to relearn the art of self-expression and consciously use words to focus your mind, to make contact with the different sides of yourself, to direct yourself and to talk deep into your soul and right out to God.

To whom are you really talking in hisbodedus — to yourself or to God? The truth is that even when you talk "to yourself," you are really talking to God. Although you experience yourself as an independent entity, at root your vitality as a living being derives from God, as does everything else in the world. All your thoughts and feelings ultimately come from God, even though they are channelled to you via the mysterious entity we call the "self" or "soul," which makes them seem to originate "inside" you.

In order to make changes in your life and grow, you must find new inner power. Fresh energy, positive mental states, insights and original ideas are all new creations that ultimately come from God, the Supreme Source of all creation. In hisbodedus you consciously reach out to God with words, songs, cries and the like in order to channel new life into yourself. When you "talk to yourself" in hisbodedus, you are at the point of encounter between your everyday self and the Supreme Power from which your very life derives.

Don't be embarrassed. You are alone and no-one can hear you. Find your own voice! Don't worry if you feel you don't know what to say. Everybody has this experience at first. Experiment with different kinds of self-expression until you discover those that have meaning for *you*.

By definition hisbodedus is a highly individual practice. You are completely unique. You must find your own way to connect with your inner "point" and with God. Tailor your hisbodedus to your own personal needs. You may use different techniques at different times depending on your mood and your needs of the moment.

Hisbodedus Techniques

relaxati
response

• **Guide Words** These are words or phrases of your choice that you repeat aloud over and over in hisbodedus in order to evoke a desired state of mind, focus your thoughts, etc. Saying words aloud or in a whisper is much more powerful than merely thinking them in your mind. Repeating the word *Shalom*, "Peace," can help calm you if you are tense. When you want to make changes in your life or achieve other important goals, keep yourself on track with guide words that express exactly what you want, (e.g. "Relax!" "Patience!" "Kindness!" "Moderation!") To develop a deeper spiritual connection, try simply repeating "God" or some other name for the Higher Power that has special meaning for you.

• **Melody** Singing or humming the right song is a powerful way to guide yourself and influence your moods and states of mind. If you are feeling uninspired, negative or depressed, choose a melody with a positive energy. When you first begin humming even a favorite song, it may take some effort to get into the right spirit. But if you persist and sing it over and over again, you will find that the melody will begin to lift you. It will bring healing rhythms into your soul, your mind and your very body. The melodies taught by outstanding spiritual teachers have the power to lift people to exalted states of consciousness and to inculcate deeper faith and trust.

Sing

• **Affirmations** Events, circumstances, other people and certain forces within ourselves often conspire to make us lose sight of essential truths. An affirmation is a statement of some important truth or belief about yourself, your goals and values, or about life in general. For example, "My goal is to heal and to live life to the full every day, every moment," or "I believe in God, and God is good," etc. Regularly making such affirmations out loud keeps these truths at the forefront of your mind. Develop your own set of affirmations about your beliefs, goals and ideals, or choose some inspiring quotations. Say them out loud regularly in your hisbodedus sessions.

• **Guiding Questions** If you want to use hisbodedus to explore yourself and resolve certain issues in your life, give focus to your quest by asking yourself guiding questions, such as "What is on my mind?" "What am I really feeling?" "Where in the world am I?" "What is my purpose in this life?" "What do I really want?" "How can I attain it?" "What keeps me locked into destructive patterns?" "What are my positive points?" etc. Asking such questions out loud can aid your concentration when exploring various issues and can also help you develop new answers.

• **Self-Expression** As you ask yourself guiding questions, many different thoughts and feelings are likely to pass through your mind. In order to understand yourself better, express what you are thinking and feeling out loud. Try to articulate your thoughts and feelings as clearly as you can. Listen carefully to what you are saying. Often we are in conflict within ourselves. Articulating the different sides of our personalities can help us explore and resolve inner conflicts. Give honest expression to all aspects of yourself, and especially to your highest ideals and aspirations. To give continuity to your mental and spiritual growth, it can be helpful to jot down some of the ideas and insights that come to you in hisbodedus and keep them in a special file.

• **Cries and tears** Little children naturally cry out in pain and hurt. You too are allowed to cry out because of your pain and to complain about the things that are troubling you. Cry to God about the pain in your body and in your soul. Cry out about your fears. Weep over your deepest hurt and sorrow. Weep for yourself. Weep for your dear ones. Weep for the world. For many people a cry of pain or an unarticulated sob rising from the depths of the heart can be their first act of outreach to God. "Where are You? God, please help me! Please *help!!!*"

• **Thanks** Don't dwell only on the negative. Think about the good things too! If you can see, hear, smell, taste, feel... thank God for it. Express your thanks out loud. "Thank you, God, that I'm breathing, I'm thinking... I may not be well, but I'm alive! I've had good times, I've done good things..." List the good things in your life. Count your blessings and thank God for them. People often associate prayer with making requests to God. But before you start asking for what you need, first give thanks to God for all the gifts and blessings you already enjoy in your life. Make it a habit to speak to God about all the different aspects of your life.

- **Requests** List your prayers and requests. Even if some of them seem unrealistic, for God anything is possible. Make detailed requests: e.g. "Please send healing to my arm, my leg, my heart, my lungs, my liver, my kidneys, etc. Help me work on my lack of conficence, low self-esteem, anger, pessimism, etc. Help me in my relationship with so and so. Help me in that situation at home or at work, etc." Pray for joy and the will to live. Ask for insight and enlightenment. Put your dreams and deepest yearnings into words, and ask God to help you attain what you want.

- **Psalms and Prayers** If you feel unable to express yourself to God or you feel that your own words are inadequate, open the Siddur (Jewish Prayer Book) or the Psalms. These are rich spiritual treasuries

---

"You must have faith that at the very moment the words of prayer leave your lips, your request is immediately answered. And if you say, 'But there are times when one's requests are not granted,' the truth is that they *are* granted, only this may be in a way that is concealed. For example, a person may ask God to take away his suffering, but the suffering may actually be beneficial in cleansing him of sin. Accordingly God answers this prayer not by removing the suffering from the person himself but by lessening the suffering in the world in general. It is an essential tenet of faith that as soon as we utter our prayers, they are answered. There is no doubt at all about this."

Rabbi Israel Baal Shem Tov

containing prayers of many different kinds expressing every mood and need in life. If you wish, open them at random and read until you find a passage that has special meaning for you. When you find such a passage, say it out loud, even several times. Leave marks in the book so that you can easily find your favorite passages another time.

Hisbodedus and Growth

Make use of the different techniques of hisbodedus according to your own personal needs each day. Life is constantly changing. New things are always happening. Our bodily states fluctuate from day to day. Our moods and our thoughts shift from minute to minute. For this reason, hisbodedus is different each time you do it.

Some people may want to launch immediately into the more active forms of self-expression such as talking directly to God. For others, quiet sitting and contemplation may often be the prime element in their hisbodedus.

No matter where you choose to put your focus, the most important thing is to practice hisbodedus regularly. The effects are cumulative. As you practice, you'll gain experience and learn how to make use of different techniques as appropriate in order to grow and accomplish what you want.

Use hisbodedus as part of your self-healing, or to work on specific problem areas in your life, whether within yourself, in your relationships, at home, in your work, in the wider community, etc. Use guiding questions and self-expression to define and understand your problems and obstacles.

Whether you want to heal yourself, make a change of lifestyle, attitudes, outlook, etc., or accomplish any other goal in life, the goal starts off as an idea in your mind. In order to turn the potential idea into an actual accomplishment, you must first develop a clear understanding of what it is you really want. Next you must work out exactly what you will have to do, step by step, in order to attain it. Then you must actually take the next step.

Hisbodedus is the time to do this work of clarifying your ideas and working out strategies for attaining your goals. The way to do it is with words. Articulate what it is you really want. Try to define the obstacles and difficulties you face. Express out loud your various ideas as to how you can overcome your problems. When you express your thoughts as clearly as possible, you can begin to see where your ideas may need further clarification.

What is up to you to do and what is up to God? Many things are in God's hands alone. All you can do is pray about them — again and again and again. Even when it comes to the things that are in your hands, you should also pray for help and the strength to actually do them. But when the time for action arrives, it's entirely up to *you*. The more you articulate your goals in hisbodedus and break them down into small, do-able steps, the easier it will be to take that next step.

The Happiness Workshop

The ultimate goal of hisbodedus is to attain happiness! If you practice hisbodedus regularly, you will soon see changes and improvements in your life. If you feel more relaxed, more optimistic and positive after a session of hisbodedus, this is the best sign that you are doing it right.

But don't expect release, insight, illumination and joy every time. Even the most assiduous practitioners of hisbodedus go through periods when they feel they are making little or no progress. Despite all their efforts, they find themselves tense, closed up, spiritually disconnected, frustrated, and unable or even unwilling to open their mouths and talk.

This is because hisbodedus is an active endeavor to elevate yourself spiritually. As soon as you face yourself as you really are and start grappling with yourself in order to take your life in hand, you will inevitably encounter powerful resisting forces. Some of these forces may be within yourself, others in the world around you. Often the resistance may become strongest when you are on the verge of a major breakthrough.

Even when you really want to talk to God, there may be times when you can think of nothing to say. At such moments simply say the word "God," or repeat the phrase, *Ribono Shel Olam*, "Master of the Universe." If you don't know who, what or where God is, or if you feel cut off spiritually, cry out: "Where are You?" If you can't speak, whisper. If you can't move your lips, say the words inside your heart.

There may be times when nothing works, no matter what you try. Sometimes things may be very bad. You may be assailed by negative thoughts. Life is full of pain and trouble. When we start examining ourselves, we may imagine that "nothing is sound from the soles of the feet to the top of the head — only wounds, bruises and festering sores" (Isaiah 1:6). We may feel that we are faced with insoluble problems on every side, while inside ourselves all we see is pain, frustration, anger, grief and contrition.

The essential work of hisbodedus is to dig and search beneath this surface negativity in order to uncover the redeeming sparks of good that exist everywhere, both in the external situations we face in our lives and within our own selves.

In the words of Rebbe Nachman: "You must seek out the good in yourself. Maybe when you start looking at yourself, it seems as if you have nothing good in you at all. Even so, don't let yourself be discouraged. Search until you find even a tiny modicum of good within yourself. Maybe when you start examining it, you feel it is full of blemishes. Even so, how is it possible that it does not contain even the tiniest amount of good? Search and search until you find some small good point in yourself that will give you new vitality and bring you to joy. And when you've found one good point, carry on searching until you find another... and then another...

"When you search for the positive points and gather them together, each good point becomes a 'note' in the melody of life. The music made by all these good points will bring life into your soul, and health and healing to your body. Then you will be able to pray and sing and give thanks to God!"

Doing it!

Hisbodedus may well turn out to be the single most important practice you adopt in order to bring your life to a higher level. Set regular times for hisbodedus. Work out the best time for you according to your schedule. Practice every day.

Sometimes people feel daunted by the idea of sitting down to meditate and pray for twenty minutes. If you find it hard to set a hisbodedus session, try it for just five minutes! Try it for even a single minute! Speak to God honestly for one minute! You'll find you can pour out many prayers even in as little as a minute!

At any time and in any place, you can always take a few moments for hisbodedus. It is

"Someone with sense and understanding should pray all his days to be able to say one true word to God, even just once in his life!"

Rebbe Nachman

always possible to snatch a little time to take a few deep breaths, offer some words of prayer, hum an inspiring melody, etc. You can do this even while washing dishes, standing in line at a checkout counter, or waiting to see a doctor, etc.

As a trial, take ten minutes for your first session of hisbodedus. You can practice hisbodedus right where you are at this very moment. Just decide that for the next ten minutes you are going to practice hisbodedus.

Spend the first five minutes sitting quietly, as discussed earlier. You might focus on your breathing or repeat a guide word such as "Shalom!" in order to settle your mind.

As you become calmer and clearer, you are ready for the second, more active phase of hisbodedus. Take a few moments to thank God for the good things in your life. Say the words out loud, or in a whisper. "Thank you for my life. Thank you for this. Thank you for that..."

Next, use guiding questions in order to become more aware of your thoughts and feelings. Ask yourself, "What am I thinking? What am I feeling? What is on my mind? What is really troubling me?" Ask these questions out loud or in a whisper.

Now start articulating your goals, needs and desires. Talk to God and to yourself about how you can attain them. You could spend five minutes or more on this active phase of hisbodedus. When you are ready to conclude, give thanks again for the good things and affirm your faith in God's ultimate goodness.

The time is now! Put this book aside and make a start!

6

Care of Your Body

You can't leave all the work of healing your body to your doctors. Most medical treatment focusses on correcting what's wrong with the body. But don't forget what's *right* with your body! How you eat and take care of yourself in other simple ways can have a vital influence on your general physical functioning. The stronger your system as a whole, the easier it will be for the sick parts to heal.

Ideally, healing should start long before the body gets sick! It's harder to restore health to a body that has been allowed to deteriorate than to maintain good health when the body is essentially sound. Sometimes it takes a bout of illness or injury to make people realize the importance of taking good care of themselves. Even so, it's never too late to start taking proper care. Make up your mind to live wisely and sensibly from now on!

"Physical health and wellbeing are part of the path to God, since it is virtually impossible for someone who is sick to have knowledge and awareness of the Creator. One must therefore avoid anything that may harm the body, and cultivate healthy habits."

Rambam

Guarding health is taught in the Bible: "Take care of yourself, and guard your soul diligently" (Deuteronomy 4:9). Physical and spiritual healthcare contribute to each other. Good physical health promotes mental and spiritual wellbeing. Conversely, spiritual wellbeing and a strong sense of mission in life make it easier to maintain the self-discipline required to keep healthy physically.

Often you have to sacrifice immediate physical gratification for the sake of long-term benefits. You have to learn to say no to your favorite bad foods or other things that are no good for you, even when they're right in front of you. You must maintain your fitness routine even when you don't feel like it.

Focus your mind on why you want to heal and keep healthy — in order to *live* your life to the full. The stronger your sense of mission and commitment to your goals, the more incentive you will have to maintain your healthcare program.

Wonders of the body

We are usually so busy going about our lives that we tend to take our physical functioning for granted. What is more wonderful than the functioning of the body — growth, renewal, self-repair, respiration, circulation, digestion, excretion of wastes, vision, hearing, smell, taste, touch, movement, coordination, etc. etc. — every second, every minute, every day for seventy, eighty, a hundred years and more!

Take a few moments to reflect on the complexity and subtlety of your body. The Jewish practice is to offer a blessing of thanks over the wonders of the body after relieving oneself: "Blessed are You, Eternal, All-Powerful God, Ruler of the universe, Who designed man with wisdom and created within him many openings and many cavities. It is revealed and known before Your Seat of Glory that if one of them is ruptured or one of them blocked, it is impossible to survive and stand before You even for a brief moment. Blessed are You, God, Who heals all flesh and acts wondrously."

Your diet

Regardless of any medications you may be taking, remember: by far the most important medicine you take into your body every day is the regular food you eat. This is what is keeping *you* going! Your diet provides the physical building blocks of your body and the energy it needs to function. Moreover, the food you eat turns into your thoughts and feelings, your moods and your mental and spiritual states.

> "What we eat and drink is a major factor in the level of happiness we experience and our ability to free ourselves of depression and anxiety."
>
> Rebbe Nachman

Everybody knows that eating badly is unhealthy for the body. Yet many people are quite unaware of the ravaging effects poor dietary patterns can have on our mental, emotional and spiritual life as well. Bad foods, or even good foods eaten badly, can cause moodswing, anxiety, negativity, fatigue and depression.

Among the main villains in our society are excesses of caffeine, sugar, fat and protein, additives, over-refined and processed foods. It's not only a matter of *what* you eat. How you space your meals through the day and combine different kinds of foods also affects your energy cycles and the way you think and feel.

Eat to feed your mind, your heart and your soul as well as your body. Eat only the finest, purest, most nourishing foods — foods that are fit to heal your physically and spiritually.

Just as some foods are good and others bad for the physical body, so there are good and bad foods for the mind and soul. This is the basis of the Jewish dietary code, which excludes impure and spiritually damaging foods, such as unclean animals, mixtures of meat with milk, etc. Acquaint yourself with the details of the Jewish dietary code.

How to eat

Good nutrition is more than a matter of chewing and swallowing your food and then forgetting all about it. The way you eat affects both the satisfaction you derive from your food and also the kind of energy and vitality it gives you.

Wherever possible, try to arrange things so that you can sit down for your meals in a relaxed state of mind. Freshen yourself and wash your hands before you eat.

As you are about to eat, don't just put the food into your mouth and bite. Pause for a moment. Reflect on the wonderful way in which this specific item of food came into being. Think about the subtle energies in the food and how they will enter your body, turning into your thoughts and feelings and your very life.

Offer your thanks to the Creator of the food. Your words of blessing before eating are the channel through which your soul receives the refined spiritual energy contained in the food.

Always chew your food carefully. Chewing is the beginning of the digestive process. Proper chewing makes for better assimilation of the nutrients in the food by the body. Thorough chewing also brings greater satisfaction, making it easier to overcome bad dietary habits. As you chew and taste your food, think about how the subtle spiritual energies in the food are being released into your body and soul.

Many people forget about what they've eaten as soon as they've swallowed it. But long after you've finished your meal, your body carries on dutifully breaking down the food, assimilating the nutrients and distributing them to all the different body parts.

So too on the mental and spiritual planes, the processes of "digestion" and "assimilation" continue as the spiritual energy in the food is released, turning into your moods, your mental states, your thoughts and feelings, words and actions.

When you are finishing your meal, these processes are just beginning. Set them off to a good start by pausing for a little while after you finish eating in order to thank God for the food and the physical and spiritual energy it contains. Remind yourself that God is taking care of you and providing for all your needs. "Eat and be satisfied, and bless HaShem, your God..." (Deuteronomy 8:10).

Exercise

Exercise should be approached with the utmost caution by those who are sick or out of condition. Anyone who is sick, in recovery or rehabilitation should exercise only under the supervision of an expert. Even those who are healthy should seek expert advice about a suitable fitness program, and follow it with the greatest care. The body is extremely subtle and delicate, and must be treated with the utmost care and respect. Sudden crash courses of exercise can be very dangerous.

On the other hand, proper exercise is one of the most important keys to good health. Exercise improves blood circulation, brings more oxygen into every cell of the body, speeds up a sluggish metabolism, enhances the functioning of internal glands and organs, improves digestion, facilitates the removal of poisonous wastes from the body, reduces the risk of many diseases, keeps joints flexible and muscles trim and strong, builds coordination and balance, heightens reflexes, reduces stress, improves sleep patterns, increases energy, and helps maintain a relaxed body and a tranquil mind.

If your daily life involves a fair amount of physical activity you may not need to devote much time to formal exercise. But if you spend much of the day sitting, you should definitely try to do some kind of exercise at least three or four times a week.

Which kind of exercise you do depends on your state of health and fitness and other individual factors. If you've not exercised for a long time and you're out of condition, you must be very patient and gentle as you slowly encourage stiff joints and muscles to start working again. People sometimes try to take a short-cut to fitness by over-straining themselves. But this can cause pain and injuries that may prevent you from exercising altogether.

"If a person cared for himself the way he cares for his horse, he would avoid many serious illnesses. You won't find anyone who gives his horse too much fodder. He measures out only as much as the horse can tolerate. But he himself eats to excess. He makes sure his animal gets proper exercise to keep it healthy. But when it comes to himself he neglects exercise even though this is a fundamental principle in health maintenance and the prevention of most illnesses."

Rambam

A balanced fitness program should include movements that promote joint flexibility and muscular endurance, and it should also include some "aerobic" exercise. This means a steady, non-stop movement that increases the pulse rate without putting strain on the cardiovascular system. Prime examples are walking (the oldest, most natural form of exercise, which utilizes almost all of your muscles); running (preferably on grass or a dirt track to reduce stress on the muscular/skeletal system and internal organs); swimming and cycling.

One of the most perfect forms of exercise is chassidic dance, in which all parts of the body are moved with grace and joy in praise of the Creator. Why not put on a recording of your favorite *nigunim* (holy melodies) and dance free-style as gently or as vigorously as you like, exploring your body and expressing your inner thoughts and feelings through your movements!

Don't forget to breathe!

The way you breathe affects your bodily health and strength, your energy levels, your calm and clarity and your mental, emotional and spiritual states. Every one of the activities of life is bound up with this fundamental process, through which the oxygen vital to our body cells enters the blood, and carbon dioxide waste is eliminated.

It will be worth your while to take a little time to explore your breathing. Familiarize yourself with the different phases of breathing. Become aware of any ingrained habits that may be inhibiting your breathing and strive to cultivate better habits. (Those who are sick should only attempt breathing work under the supervision of a medical expert.)

There is no single correct way to breathe valid for all people at all times. Obviously, physical activity requires more rapid breathing than sitting or resting. Aim to allow your breathing to adjust freely according to your specific needs at each moment. The goal should be to remove breathing malfunctions by eliminating tension and correcting the bad habits that may be causing you to inhibit the long, full, rhythmic breathing your body is geared for.

When you exhale, let your lungs empty entirely. At the end of the exhalation there is a brief pause before inhalation starts by itself. Relax your stomach and allow the air to flow in. During the inhalation, the abdominal region swells as the diaphragm lowers, drawing air into the base of the lungs. The rib-cage expands, filling the middle section of the lungs. Finally the collar bones are raised, allowing the lungs to fill to capacity.

You can practice breathing any time — at home, at work, while relaxing, waiting for buses or appointments, walking, travelling, etc. Ten long, deep breaths immediately after waking up in the morning will help banish drowsiness and heaviness and set you up for the day's activities. From time to time throughout the day, stop to re-energize with a few long, deep breaths. Deep breathing before going to bed at night will relax you and prepare you for a restful, refreshing night's sleep.

Getting dizzy from breathing exercises is a sign of hyperventilation. Use up the extra oxygen with a few vigorous movements. If the feeling persists, stop practicing deep breathing for the time being.

Concentrating on your breathing can be a powerful way of entering a state of profound calm and contemplative clarity in hisbodedus. Sit erect with your head balanced and your eyes closed. Use the relaxation technique to release all bodily tension. Now focus your awareness on your breathing. Watch each phase of the breathing process: the slow, long exhalation, the pause, the way the abdomen begins to swell and rise... Feel the cool air drawn into your nostrils and down into the lungs.

Each exhalation is actually a kind of death! It is the death of the moment that has passed, as you breathe out the stale air. But this death is a preparation for rebirth: the birth of the new moment. As you breathe out, sigh deeply and flush out all the stale air from within you. Breathe out your tensions and bad feelings. Then, as you breathe in again, focus on how you are drawing in fresh, pure, good air and breathing new life into yourself.

General healthcare

Whether you are sick or healthy, now is the time to learn to love your body and nurture it so that it becomes a fine, healthy vessel for your soul. Take the best care of yourself. Eat well. Make sure you get adequate rest and sleep. Pay careful attention to cleanliness and hygiene. Pamper your body with your favorite bodycare items.

Seek out the very best advice on healthcare. You owe it to yourself and your dear ones. If you have a medical problem, use it as a prompt to acquire a deeper understanding of your body and how to take care of it properly. Do everything possible to get the best medical attention where this is called for. If you are not satisfied with your medical treatment, ask for a second opinion.

Do whatever is in your hands to take care of yourself, and remember: the rest is up to God.

7

The Healing Process

Healing takes time. It takes time for tissues to mend, for organs to return to healthy functioning and for general physical balance to be restored. The same applies to healing the inner you, which is the very essence of the healing process. New growth, greater strength and joy will come to you over time.

The healing process will be far easier if you recognize from the outset that you are likely to experience many ups and downs physically, mentally, emotionally and spiritually. You may start feeling better and more yourself, only to experience a setback that may seem to put you back where you were before. You may go through repeated ups and downs even in the course of a single day.

Don't let reverses and obstacles throw you into despair. It is through repeated cycles of retraction and expansion that the body realigns and heals. So too on the level of self and soul, growth and development often involve repeated bouts of mental, emotional and spiritual constriction or upset. This is the way your soul marshals the inner resources you need to advance. Sinking low may indeed be a sign that you are in the process of moving to a new, higher level in your life.

When you are prepared for hard times, it makes them easier to bear. The wise King Solomon is said to have had a ring inscribed with the words, "This too will pass." He wanted to remind himself constantly that the pain, hardship and suffering of this world are only temporary. Your ability to remain patient in the face of difficulties will help you greatly during the healing process.

Two basic living skills

Two basic skills are vital in order to cope with the ups and downs of healing. The first is the skill of handling yourself well when you go up, when things are good and you feel strong and confident. It can then be very tempting to overdo things, as if you want to convince yourself that you are perfectly fit when in fact you need to take things gently. The skill of the up-phase is to enjoy it and take advantage of it, while at the same time being careful not to do anything that could impair your healing.

The second skill is knowing how to hold yourself even when you go down. You may have moments of extreme frustration and demoralization owing to your physical condition or other problems. Even if you are discouraged and depressed, don't let yourself sink into despair. Try to identify what is making you depressed. Is there any practical action you could take to help change things for the better? Even if you feel quite helpless, you still must find a way to take a more positive view of things. Have faith that God is the ultimate cause of everything you are going through, and God does only good.

Searching for the good at all times is the way to keep happy, and this is the key to true healing. The joyous song of the soul brings health and vitality to the body (see Chapter 2). Melodies and songs are made by going up and down — quite literally! The musician goes *up* and *down* on the musical scale in order to build the melody line. Whether he goes up or down, the art of making music is always to go for the good notes.

Play your life as a melody! Whether you go up or down, go for the good notes! Search out the good everywhere. Even in the darkest places, even at the hardest moments, have faith that God's goodness is everywhere and in everything.

"If you have faith in God you will have a very good life. Even in times of trouble, your faith will still inspire you. Have trust in God, and know that everything will be for the best. This world never gives people everything they desire. If you ignore your true spiritual mission and seek only the pleasures of this world, you will meet with constant frustration, and you will have nothing to console you. But when you have faith, you have hope in the life of the world to come. You therefore have a very good life in this world too, because you know that everything is for good, even your suffering. Suffering comes either to remind you to repent or to cleanse you of sin. Ultimately, it will allow you to attain the everlasting good of the world to come. But those without faith in God have no life, because their worldly troubles and anxieties completely destroy their lives."

Rebbe Nachman

Sometimes the way to break out of depression and negativity is by acting a little silly or singing out loud, and so on. If you find it hard to lift yourself out of depression, what about trying to cheer up somebody else — with a smile or a kind word or gesture?

Even when you are not in a position to help others directly, keep a charity box close by and donate even a small coin or two whenever you feel low! The concern you show for others by performing an act of charity opens a channel through which God's goodness and kindness shine into *your* soul.

At times, God's goodness may be totally hidden from you. When things are very dark, cry out and scream to God: "Where are You? Have mercy! Help me!" If all your prayers and cries

> "A person may have fallen very far. He may be sunk in the lowest pit of hell. But there is a way in which everything can be turned around for good. Therefore there is no reason to despair. No matter where you may have fallen there is still hope for you to return to God. The main thing is to *cry out*: 'From the belly of hell I cried out' (Jonah 2:3). Even a cry from the lowest depths of hell is not lost. Cry, cry and cry again! Cry and plead with God, no matter who or what you are, until God looks down from the Heavens and sees."
>
> Rebbe Nachman

and other efforts seem to be accomplishing nothing, you have no option but to heave a deep sigh and wait for things to change.

In the words of Rebbe Nachman: "Sometimes you may be disturbed by all kinds of negative thoughts and feelings. It seems impossible to overcome them. You must then make yourself like nothing. Don't even try to speak. Close your mouth. Close your eyes. Don't try to think. Your mind ceases to exist. You have totally effaced yourself. Now there is only God."

Starting again

Children learn to walk because they have an inborn instinct to get up and try again, even after falling down time after time. The ability to start all over again is necessary to accomplish anything. It is especially vital in healing and personal growth.

Even if you fall into depression and despair many times, do everything you can to pick yourself up and start again. Obstacles and difficulties of various kinds may pull you far from your goals. Perhaps you have tried prayer, hisbodedus, a new diet, a fitness program and so on, only to abandon them for some reason. But this need not mean that they are lost for ever. *You can always try again!!!*

So often people feel that right now, at this particular moment, they are simply unable to live their life the way they really want. Either circumstances are not as they would wish them to be, or they feel unwell, uncomfortable, restless, tired and depressed. So they throw away the present moment as if it doesn't really count, as if today is not one of the days of their life. They put off "real living" until later, when they hope that circumstances will improve and they will be feeling better, stronger, clearer, more relaxed, less tired.... "Tomorrow... and tomorrow... and tomorrow...."

Does that tomorrow ever come? Each new day brings its own problems and tensions. And so, one day after another is thrown away. How many minutes, hours, days, weeks, months and years of your life can you cross off and still be left with time to *live*?

You cannot afford to wait for everything to be perfect before you start living. Healing essentially means *living now*. Living is what healing is ultimately all about — for why do you want your health if not to *live* and fulfil yourself? If this is what you want, you have to take the initiative and start living *right now*.

In physical rehabilitation, when you are ready to start getting back the use of stiff, painful joints and muscles after injury or illness, the way to do it is not by waiting for them to spring miraculously back to life. No: you must gently *initiate* the process with small but increasingly adventurous movements in the right direction.

In the same way, when you want to *live*, you must start *now* by taking small, sure steps despite the fact that you may still be feeling weak, tired and disheartened.

The key is to do just a little. Try hisbodedus for just *one minute!* Sing one short nigun. Say a few words of prayer. Pick up an inspirational book and read just one paragraph. Share one kind word with someone, offer one single gesture of kindness and sympathy. Set yourself a few achievable goals for *today*, and pray to God to help you at every step.

Relax and enjoy!

The best way to live in the here and now is to take a *real holiday* as free as possible from anything unpleasant, with no hard work or errands: a day when you can just take it easy, relax, feel good and enjoy life *now!*

The idea is called Shabbat: a regular, complete holiday at the end of every week from just before sunset on Friday until just after dark on Saturday night. "Six days you may labor and do all your work, and the seventh day is Shabbat..." (Exodus 20:9).

It may be impossible to avoid all tension, depression and negativity all day, every day, seven days a week. There are always unpleasant tasks to be done, stressful situations to be faced, and so on.

But surely for one day a week you can take a holiday — a day to live and rejoice *here and now* rather than pushing off living for a tomorrow that may never come. Shabbat is a day to take a break from work, errands and other tasks and their accompanying stresses and tensions. Arrange whatever you can in advance of Shabbat in order to leave yourself free to relax and enjoy.

With nothing pressing to be done and no rush, you have *time*: time for yourself and your soul, time to be together with dear ones and friends, time to think, breathe, meditate, sing, pray, read, chat, stroll about, sit, nap, daydream... time to savor your food and drink, time to look at the world around you with new eyes, gaze up at the skies and rediscover the wonder and glory of creation.

Make Shabbat your very own holiday. Arrange your surroundings as pleasantly and comfortably as possible. Where possible, take a good bath before Shabbat. Freshen up and wear your favorite clothes. Try to have the finest foods, fine wine and other delicacies for your Shabbat meals. See that all the preparations are made in advance so that everything is ready to eat and enjoy.

Do everything possible to create an atmosphere of peace, warmth and openheartedness. Put worrisome concerns out of your mind. Think good thoughts. Speak kindly and wisely. Enjoy, and let others enjoy!

It may not be possible to avoid all tension and negativity whether in yourself or from those around you. Still, try to reduce them to an absolute minimum on Shabbat. Where those around are unable to join you in your Shabbat celebration, explain to them that Shabbat is a necessary part of your healing, and ask them to respect this.

The ultimate healing song

Celebrating Shabbat does not only affect the Shabbat day itself. The calm and enjoyment of Shabbat radiate into the weekdays that follow, giving you more inner strength to face the challenges of life. As the week progresses, you look forward to the next Shabbat. Knowing it'll soon be Shabbat again will carry you through all kinds of difficulties.

And sure enough, Shabbat arrives with its unfailing magic. As Shabbat follows Shabbat, you learn to refine and enhance the way you celebrate, so that you enjoy your Shabbat more and more.

Man is born to toil. In this world everyone has to work and struggle in some way. But work and effort are meaningless and punitive unless directed towards a worthwhile goal. The ultimate goal of work is to enjoy the fruits of one's labors. Shabbat is the time to live and enjoy. This is what gives meaning to one's work and effort during the week.

Viewing our time in this world from a broader perspective, we can describe our entire life here, with all its pain and struggle, as "six days of labor" in relation to the higher life enjoyed by the soul when our time comes to leave this world. That higher life is the true Shabbat.

Only in that higher realm can there really be perfect healing. Here in this finite, physical world, healing is always relative and at best temporary. True, many physical problems and illnesses can be more or less totally overcome; many injuries can heal completely. Indeed, the body's capacity to heal is perfectly miraculous. Even so, sooner or later every body passes its peak and starts deteriorating. The human body is simply not made to live for ever. In the end, everyone has to die.

The body is given to us in order to accomplish our unique mission in this material world, so that our higher soul may then attain the joy of the life to come. In this world the soul cannot attain perfect joy, for the simple reason that nothing in this finite, material world is perfect or everlasting. But when the time comes for the body to die, the soul is free to spread its wings and attain the boundless life and joy of the world to come. That is the true Shabbat and the ultimate healing.

Even in our life in this world we can have a *foretaste* of this future joy. It is attained through celebrating Shabbat here in this world. The weekly Shabbat experience is a "glimpse of the world to come." The vitality, goodness and pleasure we enjoy on our earthly Shabbat is a taste of the pure goodness and bliss of the future Shabbat.

This taste of the world to come has the power to sweeten any pain, hardship and struggle that may

> "We call the reward one earns in the future world 'good' because there is no other word in human speech to describe it. But it is really so much higher than any concept of good that the word is totally inadequate."
>
> Rebbe Nachman

have to be endured in this world. Why people go through pain and suffering is one off the deepest mysteries of creation. The only way to make any sense of pain, illness and death is by understanding them as a means of preparation of the soul in order to attain its ultimate destiny: the perfect Shabbat of the life after life.

Only that ultimate Shabbat gives meaning to the struggle and suffering people endure in this world. When we get a taste of that ultimate Shabbat through experiencing the enhanced vitality and joy of our weekly, earthly Shabbat, this gives us fresh strength to face up to the challenges of this world and go forward, step by step, to accomplish what we must.

"Six days of work, then Shabbat; six days of work, then Shabbat" is a rhythm of living through time. It is the primary life-giving rhythm, the rhythm that brings health and healing, spiritually and physically.

For Shabbat is the root of all true healing. The key to health and healing is the joyous melody of the soul that sends pulsating vitality into every cell of the body (see Chapter 2). The soul makes its melodies out of the "good notes" that you pick out as you go "up and down the scale" in life. The Shabbat experience gives the soul a glimpse of the ultimate good. This brings supreme joy into the soul, strengthening and vitalizing its melody.

Shabbat therefore has its own song — the song of perfect goodness:

"A psalm, a *song* for the Shabbat day. It is *good* to give thanks to God and to *sing* to Your Name, Exalted One; to tell about Your kindness in the morning and Your faithfulness in the nights. On the ten-stringed instrument and on the lyre, with singing accompanied by the harp. For You have made me *happy*, God, with Your acts, and I will *rejoice* over the work of Your hands. How great are Your works, God; very deep are Your thoughts!" (Psalms 92:1-6).

The traditional Hebrew Shabbat greeting is *Shabbat Shalom!* — "Shabbat Peace!" The "six-days-of-work, then Shabbat" rhythm brings harmony between two necessary poles of our being: the side that wants, yearns and labors for what we lack, and the side that can enjoy what we already have and give thanks for it.

When we are at harmony within ourselves, we can make our peace with those around us, with the world and with God. When we have made peace, we can truly *live*. And living is what healing is all about.

May God grant us perfect healing, healing of the soul and healing of the body. *Refu'ah shelemah, refu'at ha-nefesh u-refu'at ha-guf. Amen.*

Customs

Customs

[handwritten note in top margin: Giving charity → feel lucky to save others]

Charity

It is good for someone who is ill or in crisis to contribute to charity where possible, or for others to contribute on his or her behalf. "Charity saves from death" (Proverbs 10:2). One who is unwell is in special need of God's love. The concern one shows for others through performance of an act of charity opens a channel through which God's goodness and kindness can shine into oneself. How large a sum of money to donate depends upon one's resources. Giving small amounts frequently helps develop a kind disposition. It is a matter of personal preference as to which cause or causes to contribute, but the recipients should be worthy and genuinely needy.

*

"Redemption of the Soul" — *Pidyon Nefesh*

It is customary to send a sum of money to a *tzaddik* (outstandingly saintly person) with a request that he pray for the sick person. The tzaddik distributes the money to people in need. In Hebrew this is called *pidyon nefesh*, "redemption of the soul" of the sick individual. It is a matter of individual choice as to which tzaddik, Rebbe or spiritual leader to ask to intercede. Some people arrange for prayers to be said on behalf of the sick person at the graves of

outstanding tzaddikim of the past, such as that of
Rebbe Nachman of Breslov (located in Uman,
Ukraine), or the graves of saintly rabbis in Israel and
elsewhere, or at the Western Wall in Jerusalem.

*

Prayer

It is especially beneficial for the sick person to pray
for him/herself. It is also good for family, friends,
wellwishers and particularly children to pray for them
regularly. Such prayers may be recited in any
language. When referring to the sick person in a
prayer, it is customary to mention his or her Hebrew
name and mother's name. The traditional formula of
prayer is: "May it be Your will, my God and God of my
fathers, that You should quickly send complete healing
from Heaven — healing of the soul and healing of the
body — to (*sick person's name*), son/daughter of
(*mother's name*), among the other sick members of the
Jewish People."

On taking a medicine or receiving medical
treatment, say: "God: may it be Your will that this
medicine/treatment should bring me healing, for You
send healing as a free gift." After treatment one should
say, "Blessed is the Healer of the Sick."

*

Synagogue Prayer: *Mi she-berach...*

During the public Torah reading in the synagogue
one may arrange for a special prayer to be said for the

sick. "May He who blessed our forefathers, Abraham, Isaac and Jacob, Moses and Aaron, David and Solomon, bless and heal (*sick person's name*), son/daughter of (*mother's name*). May the Holy One, blessed-be-He, be filled with compassion and restore, heal and strengthen him/her. May He quickly send him/her complete healing of the soul and the body among the other sick people of Israel." (On Shabbat, add: "Today it is Shabbat, which is not the time to cry out. Healing will soon come!")

*

Name Change

When someone is seriously ill, it may be appropriate to give them an additional Hebrew name. One should consult a rabbi about this. Jewish mysticism teaches that a person's mission in life is bound up with their Hebrew name. Giving the person a new name sets them a new mission and may thus help extend their life. Among names frequently added are: for a male, Chaim ("Life") or Rephael (name of the angel of healing); for a female, Chayah ("Alive"). A renaming would normally take place in the course of the synagogue service.

*

Visiting the Sick — *Bikur Cholim*

Dear ones and friends should visit the sick person regularly in order to cheer him/her up and attend to any practical requirements. Visiting the sick should be an act of outreach to the *person*. The visitor must show kindness, empathy and sensitivity to the sick person's feelings, avoiding anything that might be burdensome or arouse negativity and depression. During the visit one should offer a prayer for the sick person. Where visiting is not practicable, an alternative may be to talk by phone. A phone call is a simple but powerful way to hearten and encourage someone who is feeling low.

*

Thanksgiving

On recovery from illness it is customary to recite the blessing of thanksgiving. (The blessing is usually recited during the Torah reading in the synagogue.) "Blessed are You, our God, King of the Universe, Who bestows good upon the undeserving, Who has bestowed every goodness upon me." On hearing the blessing, those present respond: "Amen. May He who has bestowed every goodness upon you continue to bestow every goodness upon you forever."

On recovery from illness, some hold a special feast of thanksgiving (*se'udat hodayah*), a festive meal attended by family and friends with blessings, prayers and songs and discussion of Torah teachings. It is especially appropriate to invite needy people to the feast or to send them portions of food.

David's Harp
Psalms and Prayers

David's Harp
Psalms and Prayers

Sometimes it's hard to find the right words with which to express ourselves at the very moments in life when something inside us yearns to reach out and connect with God.

It was to provide us with the words that King David composed the Psalms, a treasury of songs and meditations that give voice to the universal soul in each one of us.

The Psalms range from rapturous praise over the wonders of creation to cries of pain over the trials and suffering of this life; from exquisite expressions of yearning for the radiance of God's love to searingly honest self-searching; from cries and pleas for help against doubt and despair to bold affirmations of faith, courage and hope.

King David was the supreme master of music and song. He is often pictured with his harp, and is described as the "sweet singer of Israel" (II Samuel 23:1). As discussed in this book, the essential art of the musician is to pick out the good, pleasing vibrations in order to build the melodies that dispel the bad vibrations of negativity and depression (see pages 12-16).

There are many different kinds of music with many different moods. So too there are many different moods in the different songs and meditations that make up the Psalms. The original Hebrew text of the Psalms includes a complete, though little understood, musical system. According to the Kabbalah, the various different songs in the Psalms fall into ten main categories, or "Ten Types of Songs." These Ten Types of Songs have the power to sift out the hidden good that exists in all the different moments in our lives in this world, even in our worst trials and suffering.

Corresponding to the Ten Types of Songs, the Kabbalah teaches that the various different rhythms and pulses of bodily functioning fall into ten basic types of pulse patterns. Illness is bound up with a flaw in these basic bodily pulse patterns. The source of this flaw lies on the level of the "master control," which is the soul. But the Ten Types of Songs can bring new vitality into the soul, and thereby bring healing to the ten bodily pulse patterns. Since the Psalms are all based upon these Ten Types of Songs, this gives them a special healing power.

Thus the kabbalistic sages have taught that the Psalms contain prayers conducive to the health and healing of every level of the soul and every organ and system of the body. For this reason, in times of illness and crisis, people throughout the ages have turned to the book of Psalms for inspiration and spiritual healing.

While the simple, direct language of the Psalms speaks to every one of us on every level, the original Hebrew also contains profound hidden wisdom. All kinds of secret codes and messages are to be found within the Hebrew letter and vowel combinations, the musical notes and the various divine names that appear either directly or allusively. These give the Psalms multi-dimensional meaning and power.

One may read the Psalms in translation in order to give direct expression to one's inner spiritual yearnings. One may also read the Psalms in Hebrew even without understanding the meaning of the words or the hidden allusions. Simply by mouthing the letters one by one, even in a whisper, we arouse the spirit that moved the strings of David's harp. This holy spirit will lift the words and letters of our prayers straight from our mouths into God's ear.

Trust in God

Psalm 23

1. A song of David. God is my shepherd, I will not lack.

2. He lays me down in lush meadows, He leads me beside tranquil waters.

3. He restores my soul; He leads me on the paths of justice for His Name's sake.

4. Even when I walk in the valley overshadowed by death, I will fear no evil, for You are with me; Your rod and Your staff comfort me.

5. You prepare a table before me in the face of my tormentors; You have anointed my head with oil; my cup is overflowing.

6. Let only goodness and kindness pursue me all the days of my life, and let me dwell in the house of God for ever.

*

Help and protection

Psalm 121

1. A song of ascents. I raise my eyes to the mountains: from where will my help come?

2. My help is from God, Maker of heaven and earth.

3. He will not allow your foot to slip; your Guardian will not slumber.

4. See! The Guardian of Israel does not slumber or sleep.

כג

א. מִזְמוֹר לְדָוִד יְיָ רֹעִי לֹא אֶחְסָר:

ב. בִּנְאוֹת דֶּשֶׁא יַרְבִּיצֵנִי עַל־מֵי מְנוּחוֹת יְנַהֲלֵנִי:

ג. נַפְשִׁי יְשׁוֹבֵב יַנְחֵנִי בְמַעְגְּלֵי־צֶדֶק לְמַעַן שְׁמוֹ:

ד. גַּם כִּי־אֵלֵךְ בְּגֵיא צַלְמָוֶת לֹא־אִירָא רָע כִּי־אַתָּה עִמָּדִי שִׁבְטְךָ וּמִשְׁעַנְתֶּךָ הֵמָּה יְנַחֲמֻנִי:

ה. תַּעֲרֹךְ לְפָנַי שֻׁלְחָן נֶגֶד צֹרְרָי דִּשַּׁנְתָּ בַשֶּׁמֶן רֹאשִׁי כּוֹסִי רְוָיָה:

ו. אַךְ טוֹב וָחֶסֶד יִרְדְּפוּנִי כָּל־יְמֵי חַיָּי וְשַׁבְתִּי בְּבֵית־יְיָ לְאֹרֶךְ יָמִים:

*

קכא

א. שִׁיר לַמַּעֲלוֹת אֶשָּׂא עֵינַי אֶל־הֶהָרִים מֵאַיִן יָבֹא עֶזְרִי:

ב. עֶזְרִי מֵעִם יְיָ עֹשֵׂה שָׁמַיִם וָאָרֶץ:

ג. אַל־יִתֵּן לַמּוֹט רַגְלֶךָ אַל־יָנוּם שֹׁמְרֶךָ:

ד. הִנֵּה לֹא־יָנוּם וְלֹא יִישָׁן שׁוֹמֵר יִשְׂרָאֵל:

5. God is your Guardian. God is your shade at your right hand.

6. The sun will not harm you by day nor the moon by night.

7. God will protect you from all evil. He will guard your soul.

8. God will guard your going out and your coming in from now and for ever.

*

A prayer for mercy

Psalm 6

1. For the Leader, with melodies on the eight-stringed harp. A song of David.

2. God, don't rebuke me in Your anger, don't chastise me in Your rage.

3. Be kind to me, God, for I am weak; heal me, God, for my bones are shaken.

4. My soul is utterly shaken. And You, God, how long before You heal me?

5. Put aside Your anger, God. Release my soul. Save me, as befits Your kindness.

6. For there is no mention of You in death; in hell who will thank You?

7. I am exhausted from my sighs. Every night I drench my bed; with my tears I soak my couch.

8. My eye has become dim from anger and aged because of my tormentors.

ה. יְיָ שֹׁמְרֶךָ יְיָ צִלְּךָ עַל־יַד יְמִינֶךָ:

ו. יוֹמָם הַשֶּׁמֶשׁ לֹא־יַכֶּכָּה וְיָרֵחַ בַּלָּיְלָה:

ז. יְיָ יִשְׁמָרְךָ מִכָּל־רָע יִשְׁמֹר אֶת נַפְשֶׁךָ:

ח. יְיָ יִשְׁמָר־צֵאתְךָ וּבוֹאֶךָ מֵעַתָּה וְעַד־עוֹלָם:

*

ו

א. לַמְנַצֵּחַ בִּנְגִינוֹת עַל־הַשְּׁמִינִית מִזְמוֹר לְדָוִד:

ב. יְיָ אַל־בְּאַפְּךָ תוֹכִיחֵנִי וְאַל־בַּחֲמָתְךָ תְיַסְּרֵנִי:

ג. חָנֵּנִי יְיָ כִּי אֻמְלַל אָנִי רְפָאֵנִי יְיָ כִּי נִבְהֲלוּ עֲצָמָי:

ד. וְנַפְשִׁי נִבְהֲלָה מְאֹד וְאַתָּה יְיָ עַד־מָתָי:

ה. שׁוּבָה יְיָ חַלְּצָה נַפְשִׁי הוֹשִׁיעֵנִי לְמַעַן חַסְדֶּךָ:

ו. כִּי אֵין בַּמָּוֶת זִכְרֶךָ בִּשְׁאוֹל מִי יוֹדֶה־לָּךְ:

ז. יָגַעְתִּי בְּאַנְחָתִי אַשְׂחֶה בְכָל־לַיְלָה מִטָּתִי בְּדִמְעָתִי עַרְשִׂי אַמְסֶה:

ח. עָשְׁשָׁה מִכַּעַס עֵינִי עָתְקָה בְּכָל־צוֹרְרָי:

9. Leave me, all evildoers — for God has heard my weeping.

10. God has heard my plea; God will accept my prayer.

11. Let all my foes be ashamed and utterly confounded. They will regret and be instantly ashamed.

*

A cry from the depths

Psalm 38

1. A Psalm of David, to remind.

2. O God, don't rebuke me in Your anger, don't chasten me in Your wrath.

3. For Your arrows have gone deep inside me and Your hand has come down upon me.

4. There is no sound flesh in my body because of Your indignation; my bones have no peace because of my failings.

5. For my sins have gone over my head; like a weighty burden, they are too heavy for me.

6. My wounds have turned putrid, they are festering as a result of my folly.

7. I'm bent and bowed down terribly; all day I go about in mourning.

8. In the depths of my being I'm filled with a sense of worthlessness, and nothing is sound in my body.

ט. סוּרוּ מִמֶּנִּי כָּל־פֹּעֲלֵי אָוֶן כִּי־שָׁמַע יְיָ קוֹל בִּכְיִי:

י. שָׁמַע יְיָ תְּחִנָּתִי יְיָ תְּפִלָּתִי יִקָּח:

יא. יֵבֹשׁוּ וְיִבָּהֲלוּ מְאֹד כָּל־אֹיְבָי יָשֻׁבוּ יֵבֹשׁוּ רָגַע:

*

לח

א. מִזְמוֹר לְדָוִד לְהַזְכִּיר:

ב. יְיָ אַל־בְּקֶצְפְּךָ תוֹכִיחֵנִי וּבַחֲמָתְךָ תְיַסְּרֵנִי:

ג. כִּי־חִצֶּיךָ נִחֲתוּ בִי וַתִּנְחַת עָלַי יָדֶךָ:

ד. אֵין־מְתֹם בִּבְשָׂרִי מִפְּנֵי זַעְמֶךָ אֵין־שָׁלוֹם בַּעֲצָמַי מִפְּנֵי חַטָּאתִי:

ה. כִּי עֲוֹנֹתַי עָבְרוּ רֹאשִׁי כְּמַשָּׂא כָבֵד יִכְבְּדוּ מִמֶּנִּי:

ו. הִבְאִישׁוּ נָמַקּוּ חַבּוּרֹתָי מִפְּנֵי אִוַּלְתִּי:

ז. נַעֲוֵיתִי שַׁחֹתִי עַד־מְאֹד כָּל־הַיּוֹם קֹדֵר הִלָּכְתִּי:

ח. כִּי־כְסָלַי מָלְאוּ נִקְלֶה וְאֵין מְתֹם בִּבְשָׂרִי:

9. I'm exhausted and utterly crushed; I groan because of the turbulence in my heart.

10. O God: all my desperate craving is known to You; my sighing is not hidden from You.

11. My heart is closed up with sadness, my strength has left me. The light of my eyes has also gone from me.

12. My dear ones and friends stand aloof from my suffering, and those who were near me stand far away.

13. Those who want my life are plotting against me; those who seek to harm me tell lies and think treacherous thoughts all day.

14. But I am like a deaf person — I don't hear; I am like a dumb person who does not open his mouth.

15. I am like a man who does not hear, and in whose mouth are no complaints.

16. For my hope is in You, O God; You will answer, my Master and my God.

17. For I said in my heart, 'Lest they rejoice over my downfall; lest they speak arrogantly when my foot slips.'

18. For I am all too familiar with suffering, and my pain is with me continually.

19. For I admit my wrongdoing, I am full of anxiety because of my sins,

20. While my enemies are strong and healthy, and those who hate me wrongfully have multiplied.

ט. נְפוּגֹתִי וְנִדְכֵּיתִי עַד־מְאֹד שָׁאַגְתִּי מִנַּהֲמַת לִבִּי:

י. אֲדֹנָי נֶגְדְּךָ כָל־תַּאֲוָתִי וְאַנְחָתִי מִמְּךָ לֹא־נִסְתָּרָה:

יא. לִבִּי סְחַרְחַר עֲזָבַנִי כֹחִי וְאוֹר־עֵינַי גַּם־הֵם אֵין אִתִּי:

יב. אֹהֲבַי וְרֵעַי מִנֶּגֶד נִגְעִי יַעֲמֹדוּ וּקְרוֹבַי מֵרָחֹק עָמָדוּ:

יג. וַיְנַקְשׁוּ מְבַקְשֵׁי נַפְשִׁי וְדֹרְשֵׁי רָעָתִי דִּבְּרוּ הַוּוֹת וּמִרְמוֹת כָּל־הַיּוֹם יֶהְגּוּ:

יד. וַאֲנִי כְחֵרֵשׁ לֹא אֶשְׁמָע וּכְאִלֵּם לֹא יִפְתַּח־פִּיו:

טו. וָאֱהִי כְּאִישׁ אֲשֶׁר לֹא־שֹׁמֵעַ וְאֵין בְּפִיו תּוֹכָחוֹת:

טז. כִּי־לְךָ יְיָ הוֹחָלְתִּי אַתָּה תַעֲנֶה אֲדֹנָי אֱלֹהָי:

יז. כִּי־אָמַרְתִּי פֶּן־יִשְׂמְחוּ־לִי בְּמוֹט רַגְלִי עָלַי הִגְדִּילוּ:

יח. כִּי־אֲנִי לְצֶלַע נָכוֹן וּמַכְאוֹבִי נֶגְדִּי תָמִיד:

יט. כִּי־עֲוֹנִי אַגִּיד אֶדְאַג מֵחַטָּאתִי:

כ. וְאֹיְבַי חַיִּים עָצֵמוּ וְרַבּוּ שֹׂנְאַי שָׁקֶר:

21. Those who repay good with evil hate me because of my pursuit of good.

22. Don't abandon me, Eternal God, don't be far from me!

23. Quickly help me, God of my salvation!

*

Protection

Psalm 91

May the pleasantness of God be upon us. Establish the work of our hands for us! Establish the work of our hands.

1. Whoever sits in the refuge of the Most High shall dwell in the shadow of the Almighty.

2. I say of God, 'He is my refuge and my fortress — my God — I will trust in Him.'

3. For He will save you from the ensnaring trap and from devastating pestilence.

4. With His pinion He will cover you, and beneath His wings you will find refuge; His truth will protect you like a shield and armor.

5. You will have no fear of the terror of night or of the arrow that flies by day;

6. Nor of the pestilence that walks in gloom; nor the destroyer that wreaks destruction in the middle of the day.

כא. וּמְשַׁלְּמֵי רָעָה תַּחַת טוֹבָה יִשְׂטְנוּנִי תַּחַת רָדְפִי־
טוֹב:

כב. אַל־תַּעַזְבֵנִי יְיָ אֱלֹהַי אַל־תִּרְחַק מִמֶּנִּי:

כג. חוּשָׁה לְעֶזְרָתִי אֲדֹנָי תְּשׁוּעָתִי:

*

צא

וִיהִי נֹעַם אֲדֹנָי אֱלֹהֵינוּ עָלֵינוּ, וּמַעֲשֵׂה יָדֵינוּ כּוֹנְנָה
עָלֵינוּ, וּמַעֲשֵׂה יָדֵינוּ כּוֹנְנֵהוּ:

א. יֹשֵׁב בְּסֵתֶר עֶלְיוֹן בְּצֵל שַׁדַּי יִתְלוֹנָן:

ב. אֹמַר לַיהֹוָה מַחְסִי וּמְצוּדָתִי אֱלֹהַי אֶבְטַח־בּוֹ:

ג. כִּי הוּא יַצִּילְךָ מִפַּח יָקוּשׁ מִדֶּבֶר הַוּוֹת:

ד. בְּאֶבְרָתוֹ יָסֶךְ לָךְ וְתַחַת־כְּנָפָיו תֶּחְסֶה צִנָּה וְסֹחֵרָה
אֲמִתּוֹ:

ה. לֹא־תִירָא מִפַּחַד לָיְלָה מֵחֵץ יָעוּף יוֹמָם:

ו. מִדֶּבֶר בָּאֹפֶל יַהֲלֹךְ מִקֶּטֶב יָשׁוּד צָהֳרָיִם:

7. Even if a thousand destroyers encamp at your left side and ten thousand at your right, they will not come close to you.

8. Just look with your eyes and you will see the retribution of the wicked.

9. Because you said, 'You, God, are my refuge,' and you have made the Most High your safe dwelling place.

10. No evil will befall you and no plague will come near your tent.

11. He will charge His angels to protect you in all your ways.

12. They will carry you in their hands, lest you strike your foot against a stone.

13. You will tread upon the lion and the viper and they will not hurt you; you will trample the young lion and serpent.

14. [God says]: For he has yearned for Me and I will deliver him; I will lift him up, for he knows My Name.

15. He will call upon Me and I will answer him. I am with him in distress. I will save him and give him honor.

16. I will satisfy him with long life and show him My salvation.

*

ז. יִפֹּל מִצִּדְּךָ אֶלֶף וּרְבָבָה מִימִינֶךָ אֵלֶיךָ לֹא יִגָּשׁ:

ח. רַק בְּעֵינֶיךָ תַבִּיט וְשִׁלֻּמַת רְשָׁעִים תִּרְאֶה:

ט. כִּי־אַתָּה יְיָ מַחְסִי עֶלְיוֹן שַׂמְתָּ מְעוֹנֶךָ:

י. לֹא־תְאֻנֶּה אֵלֶיךָ רָעָה וְנֶגַע לֹא־יִקְרַב בְּאָהֳלֶךָ:

יא. כִּי מַלְאָכָיו יְצַוֶּה־לָּךְ לִשְׁמָרְךָ בְּכָל־דְּרָכֶיךָ:

יב. עַל־כַּפַּיִם יִשָּׂאוּנְךָ פֶּן־תִּגֹּף בָּאֶבֶן רַגְלֶךָ:

יג. עַל־שַׁחַל וָפֶתֶן תִּדְרֹךְ תִּרְמֹס כְּפִיר וְתַנִּין:

יד. כִּי בִי חָשַׁק וַאֲפַלְּטֵהוּ אֲשַׂגְּבֵהוּ כִּי־יָדַע שְׁמִי:

טו.יִקְרָאֵנִי וְאֶעֱנֵהוּ עִמּוֹ־אָנֹכִי בְצָרָה אֲחַלְּצֵהוּ וַאֲכַבְּדֵהוּ:

טז. אֹרֶךְ יָמִים אַשְׂבִּיעֵהוּ וְאַרְאֵהוּ בִּישׁוּעָתִי:

*

Thanksgiving
Psalm 30

1. A song for the consecration of the Temple, by David.

2. I will exalt You, God, for You have drawn me up and not let my foes rejoice over me.

3. Eternal Master, my God, I cried out to You and You healed me.

4. God, You have lifted my soul out of hell. You have saved me from going down into the pit.

5. Sing to God, His devout ones, and give thanks to His Holy Name.

6. For His anger is only for a moment, but His favor brings life. In the evening one may weep, but with morning comes joy!

7. When I was at peace I said, 'I will never falter.'

8. But God, everything is through Your favor. It is You who established me on my mountain of strength, yet if You conceal Your face I would be confounded.

9. To You, God, I call, and to my Master I appeal.

10. What will be gained if I die and go down to destruction? Will the dust acknowledge You? Will it declare Your truth?

11. Hear, God, and be kind to me; God, be my Helper.

12. You have transformed my sorrow into dancing. You took off my sackcloth and girded me with joy.

13. So that my soul might sing to You and not be muted, my Eternal God, I will thank You forever.

ל

א. מִזְמוֹר שִׁיר־חֲנֻכַּת הַבַּיִת לְדָוִד:

ב. אֲרוֹמִמְךָ יְיָ כִּי דִלִּיתָנִי וְלֹא שִׂמַּחְתָּ אֹיְבַי לִי:

ג. יְיָ אֱלֹהָי שִׁוַּעְתִּי אֵלֶיךָ וַתִּרְפָּאֵנִי:

ד. יְיָ הֶעֱלִיתָ מִן־שְׁאוֹל נַפְשִׁי חִיִּיתַנִי מִיָּרְדִי־בוֹר:

ה. זַמְּרוּ לַיהוָֹה חֲסִידָיו וְהוֹדוּ לְזֵכֶר קָדְשׁוֹ:

ו. כִּי רֶגַע בְּאַפּוֹ חַיִּים בִּרְצוֹנוֹ בָּעֶרֶב יָלִין בֶּכִי וְלַבֹּקֶר רִנָּה:

ז. וַאֲנִי אָמַרְתִּי בְשַׁלְוִי בַּל־אֶמּוֹט לְעוֹלָם:

ח. יְיָ בִּרְצוֹנְךָ הֶעֱמַדְתָּה לְהַרְרִי עֹז הִסְתַּרְתָּ פָנֶיךָ הָיִיתִי נִבְהָל:

ט. אֵלֶיךָ יְיָ אֶקְרָא וְאֶל־אֲדֹנָי אֶתְחַנָּן:

י. מַה־בֶּצַע בְּדָמִי בְּרִדְתִּי אֶל שַׁחַת הֲיוֹדְךָ עָפָר הֲיַגִּיד אֲמִתֶּךָ:

יא. שְׁמַע־יְיָ וְחָנֵּנִי יְיָ הֱיֵה־עֹזֵר לִי:

יב. הָפַכְתָּ מִסְפְּדִי לְמָחוֹל לִי פִּתַּחְתָּ שַׂקִּי וַתְּאַזְּרֵנִי שִׂמְחָה:

יג. לְמַעַן יְזַמֶּרְךָ כָבוֹד וְלֹא יִדֹּם יְיָ אֱלֹהַי לְעוֹלָם אוֹדֶךָ:

Other Psalms that are particularly appropriate in time of illness include: 13, 20, 39, 41, 88 and 92.

Rebbe Nachman of Breslov taught that there are ten Psalms that contain all the Ten Types of Songs. He called these Psalms the "General Remedy" (*Tikun HaKlali*). The ten Psalms are: 16, 32, 41, 42, 59, 77, 90, 105, 137 and 150.

The following extracts are from the prayers of Rabbi Nathan, leading disciple of Rebbe Nachman.

*

Happiness and joy

Loving God, Master of the Universe, Source of happiness and joy. In Your presence there is only joy. "Glory and majesty are before Him, might and delight are in His place."

Kind and loving God, teach me the path of life and help me to be happy at all times. You know how far I am from true joy. I therefore appeal to You, loving God: help me attain true happiness. Show me the path to follow. Break the hold of depression over me. Teach me a way to turn my very sadness and depression into joy.

If at any time I begin to become depressed, let me rejoice over the fact that You still love me. You have kept me alive and You have not let me slip completely. Maybe I am far from God; I may have many shortcomings. Even so, if I examine myself and my life carefully, I *can* find good within myself. Every day I have the opportunity to perform many mitzvot and good deeds. This is a good reason to be happy.

Master of the Universe: Let me use every possible means to bring joy into my heart, whether by thinking about my good points, through playfulness and joking, or even by putting on a *show* of being lighthearted when necessary.

Bring me to follow Your pathways joyously, with a heart flowing with appreciation of Your abundant goodness. Let me make it a habit to put myself in a good mood by singing joyous songs. Let me fill myself with the Ten Kinds of Songs, which encompass all true joy. I'll sing out and rejoice in God with songs, praises, gladness and melody, and I'll always be happy. And through this, put a spirit of holy vitality into the pulses that beat within me, so as to guard and protect me from any kind of pain and illness, physical or spiritual.

Heal all our illnesses and cure all our pains and sores. Heal our souls and our bodies. Heal us, O God, and we will be healed, save us and we will be saved, for You are our praise!

*

Sweeten the bitterness

Master of the World! Master of the entire Universe! You know the bitterness of my heart, the bitterness of my terrible wounds, and the bitterness of my crushed soul.

Be kind to me and sweeten the bitterness. Show me the Tree of Life with which to sweeten the bitter waters. Compassionate God: remove every kind of bitterness from me, and give me strength, power and courage to bear with love the little bitterness that I must inevitably suffer in order to be healed. Merciful God, minimize the bitterness needed to cure me as far as possible, and quickly send me complete healing, spiritually and physically.

From afar I can see the infinite mercy with which You treat me at every moment. That is why I am casting my burden upon You alone. Have mercy on me. Protect me. Spread Your tabernacle of peace over me. Send perfect healing to all the wounds and diseases of my soul and body. Fulfil in me the verse: "'Peace! peace, to the one who is far off and the one who is near,' says God, Who creates the fruit of the lips, and I will heal him."

*

Faith

Master of the Universe! Compassionate God! Help me rid myself of doubts and questions and develop perfect faith. Let me strengthen my faith to the utmost, and believe in You and Your Torah with strong, firm, clear, pure faith without any doubts or questions at all.

Give me faith in the power of prayer. Heavenly Father, You know how hard it is for me to open my mouth to pray. My prayers are full of flaws. I'm like a dumb person. Open Your mouth to me. "God, open my lips and my mouth will declare Your praise." Make my heart ready, and turn Your ear to me.

Help me put my whole heart and soul into my prayers. Nothing in the world is more exalted than prayer. Let my every prayer be an appeal for Your love and kindness. Let me never feel my prayers to be a burden. Let me make every possible effort to concentrate all my thoughts and feelings on my prayers.

Prayer is the channel for all true healing. Through my prayers, help me draw healing to myself and to all others in need of healing. Draw healing power into our very bread and water and all our other food and drink, and fulfil Your promise: "And He will bless your bread and water, and remove sickness from among you" (Exodus 23:25).

Lovingly send us complete healing, physically and spiritually. Heal all of our two hundred and forty-eight limbs and three hundred and sixty-five arteries and veins. For You alone know all our pains and illnesses — those of which we are aware and those that are hidden from us. Have pity on us and send us the remedy even before the blow. As soon as an illness starts developing, send us complete healing before it spreads.

You alone have the power to heal us, for we have no way of healing our wounds and illnesses — not when they're still concealed, and not when they begin to manifest themselves. We depend on You alone, and we are waiting and hoping for You to heal us.

You have the power to work awesome miracles. Send us complete healing from heaven and remove sickness from our midst. For You are God, the King, the faithful and loving Healer. Heal us, O God and we will be healed, save us and we will be saved, for You are our praise.

*

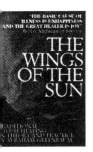

The Wings of the Sun
Traditional Jewish Healing in Theory and Practice
by Avraham Greenbaum

A clear, informative study of teachings on healing in the Bible, Talmud, Kabbalah and the Chassidut of Rebbe Nachman. Kabbalah view of the human body. The Ten Pulses & Ten Kinds of Songs. Prayer. Meditation. Diet. Exercise. Facing illness. Recovery.

.75" x 9.2". 468 pages. Softback. ISBN 0-930213-53-X. **$20**

Under the Table and How to Get Up
Jewish Pathways of Spiritual Growth
by Avraham Greenbaum

Rebbe Nachman's funny but profound parable of the prince who thought he was a turkey provides the framework for this handbook of easy-to-apply teachings on how to develop the higher self.

.5" x 8.5". 289 pages. Softback. ISBN 0-930213-41-6. **$12**

Garden of the Souls: Rebbe Nachman on Suffering

Guidance and comfort in dealing with pain and suffering.

' x 8". 96 pages. Softback. ISBN 0-930213-39-4. **$7**

Restore My Soul

How to draw from the wellsprings of joy and spiritual strength.

.5" x 6.5". 128 pages. Softback. ISBN 0-930213-13-0. **$4**

To order: phone, fax, mail or e-mail to
The Breslov Research Institute:

Israel: PO Box 5370, Jerusalem 91 500. Tel. 02-582 4641.

North America: POB 587, Monsey, NY 10952-0587. Tel: 914-425-4258; Fax: 914-425-3018

Britain: 24 B St. Paul's Ave, Kenton, Harrow, Middx HA3 OPS. Tel: 0181-357-2392

e-mail: sales@breslov.org

All set prices include shipping/handling. Prices subject to change. Make checks payable to Breslov Research Institute.

Music for the Soul!

Niguney Gan Eden

Cassette tape of traditional chassidic melodies for spiritual connection and healing.

Sung and played by Avraham ben Yakov

U.S.: $10 ✦ **Canada:** $13 ✦ **Britain:** £6.50

♦ ♦ ♦ ♦ ♦ ♦ ♦ ♦ ♦ ♦ ♦ ♦

A Call to Live

A gift to touch the hearts of dear ones and friends facing illness! Take a copy when you visit, or have one sent direct.

U.S.: $10 ✦ **Canada:** $13 ✦ **Britain:** £6.50

♦ ♦ ♦ ♦ ♦ ♦ ♦ ♦ ♦ ♦ ♦ ♦

To order: phone, fax, mail or e-mail to

The Azamra Institute:

Israel: PO Box 50037, Jerusalem 91 500. Tel/Fax: (02) 537-0064

United States: 119 Rockland Center, Suite 148, Nanuet, NY 10954. Tel. 914-425-1965. Fax. 914-425-3018

Canada: Box 5696, Station A, 25 The Esplanade, Toronto, Ontario M5W 1N8. Tel: 416-537 2671. Fax: 416-594 3369

Britain: 24 B St. Paul's Ave, Kenton, Harrow, Middx HA3 OPS. Tel: 0181-357-2392

E-mail: orders@azamra.org

All set prices include shipping/handling. Generous discounts on quantity orders. Prices subject to change.

Make checks payable to The Azamra Institute. U.S. and Canadian orders may be paid with credit card.